Niède & Mignonne
All the best
to both of you.
J'espoire que
vous aimerez
cette livre.
Your
Wilfred
June 28/92.

Sharing the *LOVE*
that frees us

a spiritual awakening
from the struggles of
addiction and abuse

Wilfred A. Gallant
Ed. D., M.S.W., C.A.D.C.
University of Windsor

CAPTUS PRESS

Sharing the Love that Frees Us: A Spiritual Awakening
from the Struggles of Addiction and Abuse

Canadian Cataloguing in Publication Data

Gallant, Wilfred Alexander, 1943–
    Sharing the love that frees us
Includes bibliographical references.
ISBN 0–921801–99–8

1. Brentwood Recovery Home. 2. Alcoholism —
Treatment — Ontario — Whitby. 3. Substance abuse —
Treatment — Ontario — Whitby. 4. Church work with
alcoholics — Ontario — Whitby. 5. Church work with
narcotics addicts — Ontario — Whitby. I. Title.

HV5283.C32W48 1992   362.29'186'0971356   C92–094482–5

First Captus Press edition, 1992

Rear cover photo: Kaiser Photography, Windsor, Ont.

0 9 8 7 6 5 4 3 2 1
Printed and bound in Canada

To my two beautiful daughters, Jennifer and Melanie, whose quality of life has touched me profoundly. In their still, quiet presence and in their joyful sense of celebration, I am able to appreciate ever more richly the excitement of youth and the challenge of life that lies before all of us. They are a real gift to me!

TABLE OF CONTENTS

This book was written as a result of an exploratory study of Brentwood while I was on sabbatical during the 1989–90 academic year. It attempts to describe the philosophy, history and rehabilitation program in Windsor, Ontario as communicated to me by Fr. Paul Charbonneau, Kay and Jim Ryan and the staff and alumni who work there. This study was undertaken to provide a clearer insight into Brentwood's approach to alcoholism and alcoholism recovery and to furnish a greater awareness of the Brentwood phenomenon—its *process of recovery*, (*"people needing people"*), where the *spiritual orientation* replaces the need for alcohol, drugs or process addiction.

Because the Brentwood program has proven successful in the lives of addicted people and dysfunctional families, it is hoped that this book may in some way prove beneficial for anyone wishing to help such people. It may also assist potential helpers to understand the use of a spiritually healing dimension by means of the personal presence of one person to another and help social agencies, churches, clergy and religious support groups and workplaces which have an Employee Assistance Program (EAP). The contents of these pages will ring true for the ordinary lay person who has been lost and afflicted within a dysfunctional family or with any kind of addiction whether it be to alcohol, drugs, gambling, sex, work, religion, overeating, smoking or violence, and who are involved in some type of mutual self-help group.

Faculty teaching in medicine, psychology, social work and education may find here a means of exposing their students to a spiritual, therapeutic and holistic model of recovery based upon Father Paul Charbonneau's twenty-five years of experience. The Brentwood model presents an invitation for others in the mental health field to rethink their own perceptions of alcoholism and addiction. The findings of this study will hopefully provide a basis for more thorough and scientific research on Brentwood's mode of recovery so as to pass the test of time.

The words and phrases underlined in the text are from the traditional words used by Fr. Paul, the staff and the residents in their communication about elements of the program. The word "alcoholic" and alumni are used in the generic sense to encompass both the male and the female gender. The reason for this generic approach is to expedite the reading of the material and to eliminate distractions which would be readily caused by the inclusion of "he/she, himself/herself, him/her" type of terminology. The use of the plural form instead of the singular has been used where appropriate and as recommended by the APA, the American Psychological Association, to reduce gender preference or any sex stereotyping.

W.A.G.
March, 1992

ACKNOWLEDGEMENTS

I am deeply grateful to the countless individuals who have made this book possible. First and foremost to Fr. Paul Charbonneau from whom this work has its genesis, to Jim and Kay Ryan for their invaluable help and to Fr. Bob Charbonneau, Fr. Paul's brother, for his patience and contribution to the numerous revisions of the manuscript. I am particularly indebted to Sam Devin for his assistance with Chapter 1, and to the staff and alumni who have so generously provided me with their countless insights. I wish to express appreciation to the University of Windsor for the research time that was made available to me during my sabbatical year. I must acknowledge my indebtedness to Rev. Roland Janisse, Dr. Tom Schuman and Laura Rosenthal for their painstaking review of the manuscript. I would like to express thanks to Dr. Pat Ryan for his invaluable assistance with Chapter 1. I want to give special recognition to Dr. Forrest (Bud) Hansen for his enlightening support on the analysis of the research questionnaire and for his insightful contribution to Chapter 8. Dr. Jay Conger and Dr. Rabindra Kanungo of McGill University are remembered appreciatively for their influence and support in providing the tools to help me determine if Fr. Paul was perceived as a charismatic leader by his followers. Countless alumni have contributed to this work and must remain anonymous, particularly the group leaders who were helpful in my interviews with them. I want to express gratitude to His Eminence, Emmet Cardinal Carter, Archbishop Marcel Gervais, Bishops Fred Henry and John Sherlock, for their time and personal investment in allowing me to interview them. I would also like to thank Frank D'Angelo for his creative input for the book's title.

W.A.G.
March, 1992

Brentwood in Brief

Brentwood is a rehabilitation centre for the treatment of people with alcohol and drug-related problems and has been serving the community since 1964. It began as a small 10-bed facility serving meals to transients and providing beds for alcoholics. Today, Brentwood has grown into a 200-bed rehabilitation centre, providing inpatient, outpatient, day care and school education programs to both men and women from the community. Brentwood is the largest centre of its kind in Canada. Referrals are accepted from hospitals, physicians, community agencies, companies, families and self-referrals.

Brentwood believes that alcoholics centre life around themselves and that they act in an overly independent way in order to deny that they are dependent on alcohol. Support and guidance are provided to those clients who have a sincere desire to rid themselves of their alcoholic and drug dependencies. Assessment prior to admission is required in order to determine an individual's suitability for the program and includes a discussion with a senior person on program and a tour of the facility.

Brentwood's highly successful program offers both individual and group therapy. Clients benefit from the guidance of professionally trained staff with expertise in addictions. In addition, they have the opportunity to learn from the experiences of others who have achieved sobriety. Structured group sessions are designed to bring out the feelings and emotions that every alcoholic experiences. Having done this, clients can begin, with help and encouragement, to take responsibility for their own lives.

Brentwood offers a full range of counselling services to the families of program participants. Spouses, children and parents are helped to cope with existing family problems and learn about recovery of the relative who is undergoing treatment. Its "total family care" approach affords the client every opportunity to return to a full and meaningful life.

Alumni are an important part of the treatment process and are involved in every aspect of Brentwood's operation. The greater number of treatment staff are recovered alcoholics who have been through the program. Brentwood adheres to the principle that the recovered alcoholic

1

is the best person to reach and help the alcoholic. A first-rate team of support staff, including social workers and psychologists, work with and assist the alcoholic and the family with a variety of problems.

Friendship and support continues after the treatment is completed. Some clients continue in an outpatient and/or day care setting. Special programs are designed for alumni and their families to help ensure continued sobriety. A special program is provided for the children on a weekly basis.

CHAPTER 1

Brentwood's Perception of Alcoholism and Addiction

How does one comprehend the nature of addictive behaviour? The Brentwood model of recovery is designed to apply equally well to the major incessant, obsessive behaviour found in alcoholism, substance abuse and addiction. There is a recurrent need to be vigilant in the field of recovery since popular magazines seem to have an increasing monopoly on offering "instant cures" for any conceivable ailment imaginable. Brentwood's perception of alcoholism will be considered first, to be followed by its perception of addiction.[1]

Alcoholism

The Brentwood Definition of Alcoholism

Brentwood is gaining recognition as a viable treatment facility in Ontario and, indeed, in all of Canada for people with addiction-related issues. Its daily admission rate is on the increase as is its treatment of youth. Brentwood admits that though this model is not a perfect one, it *does* work and that there are thousands of alumni who can attest to its glowing success by the quality of their lives today.

Though Brentwood views alcoholism as a "spiritual disease", it goes beyond the narrow disease concept to the existential cause and it attacks the heart of the disease in the pragmatic and phenomenological sense of the term. More appropriately, Brentwood deals with the concept of disease in a more metaphorical sense by comparing it to cancer or to kidney failure. Its emphasis is on the personal and social ramifications of this "spiritual affliction". Brentwood seeks to uncover the beginning or embryonic stage which predisposes the alcoholic to the disorder. It is seen as an ailment which not only threatens others but also alienates

---

1.   This chapter uses the word "alcoholic" and "addicted" interchangeably so that the word "alcoholic" is covered under the umbrella of an addictive syndrome.

3

the alcoholic from the self, the real world and from God and nature. The word "alcoholic" is a blanket expression or an umbrella term which covers the whole gamut not only of addiction but of the underlying cause of the addictive syndrome. The heart of the disease is seen within the alcoholic's distortion of reality and the compulsive regression which hampers normal growth and development. At Brentwood, alcoholism is considered to be primarily an addiction and a dependency to a substance, whether a physical or a psychological dependence, which impedes normal thinking, feeling and behavioural functioning of the person and which renders the individual unable to love.

Comparison with Traditional Psychiatric and Other Definitions[2]

Although the Brentwood philosophy takes a non-medical view of alcoholism, it is still important to have an understanding of its unique approach and to be able to compare its definition with both traditional psychiatry and the other mental health professions. To begin with, it would be more accurate to say that the Brentwood philosophy, and more particularly Fr. Paul, is interested in the alcoholic individual, not in the abstraction of alcoholism per se. Even though this is the case, and defining alcoholism has not been a priority, the two sets of definitions, Brentwood's and the traditional mental health community's, are parallel and not mutually exclusive. That is, there is nothing in the traditional "psychiatric view" that is seriously contrary to the Brentwood philosophy. There is a recognition, for example, that there could be a biological basis for alcoholism in light of the strong tendency of alcoholism to follow family lines. Of course, the psychosocial theorists would argue that the familial trend is proof of the psychosocial roots of the disorder. The truth probably encompasses both views. Being the recipient of alcoholic genes or being raised by an alcoholic with no blood relationship both arguably have an effect on the outcome of personality development. The "nature vs nurture" dichotomy has long been abandoned as a false distinction by most behavioural scientists. The interaction between heredity and environmental issues is currently not well understood and may not even be fully understood into the next century. Psychobiology and sociobiology are immature scientific disciplines at best, and have little to contribute to the practicing clinician (Ryan, 1990).

Historically, one competing theory of a disease, disorder or other phenomena never achieves primacy over the other. They blend at some point to become a unified theory and one wonders why, in retrospect, the obvious contribution of both to the final product was not clearly seen by the earlier theorists. An example from our recent past is the theory of neurosis. Freud, the father of psychoanalysis, felt that all neuroses

2.   I am indebted to Dr. Pat Ryan, clinical psychologist at Brentwood for his comparison of Brentwood, traditional psychiatry and other mental health professional definitions.

would eventually be seen as arising from biochemical defects in the central nervous system. Nonetheless, he developed a purely psychological theory that has stood for more than a century. Granted, biological psychiatry has elaborated on the physiology and chemistry of many of the psychiatric disorders but molecular biology has not supplanted the psychological and social theories. Rather, the theories exist in harmony as clinicians are more accepting of the fact of multiple causation for psychiatric disorders (Ryan, 1990).

Let us examine the psychiatric criteria for the diagnosis of alcoholism, noting that the diagnostic criteria are still in transition. The psycho-diagnostic focus still is and must remain strongly behavioural— and symptom-oriented. The causes of the disorder are still neglected. The issue of the alcoholic personality has been put on the back burner. Lisansky's bold assertion in 1967 that all alcoholics had in common was a tendency to drink too much has had a chilling effect in the scientific community with regard to further exploration of commonalities among alcoholics. Her difficulty in establishing commonality of constellations of personality traits for the disorder may have had more to do with definitions and with the methods of research than with a factual basis for the lack of scientific support for an alcoholic personality style. The other possibility, not of common personality, but of common traumatic early life experiences and consequent developmental failures is a road less travelled but probably more fruitful in terms of research results that make sense. Our experience with the Vietnam war and Post-traumatic Stress Disorder have given us a parallel of what the effects of prolonged exposure to stress can do to human behaviour. The effects are probably more profound and confounded in the developing child exposed to stresses during critical developmental task periods. The alcoholic personality has much in common with chronic post-traumatic stress disorder from a causal perspective and also from the point of view of an erratic and bewildering set of symptoms, not all of which need to be present to make the diagnosis. The diagnosis at Brentwood is often made by reference to the person's childhood experiences and the trauma that beset them (Ryan, 1990).

The DSM 111 Separates Alcoholism into Alcohol Abuse and Alcohol Dependence

1. *Alcohol Abuse*

   A. Pattern of pathological use: the need for daily use of alcohol for adequate functioning, inability to cut down or stop drinking, repeated efforts to cut down or go on the wagon or restricting drinking to certain times of the day; binges; occasional consumption of a fifth of spirits or beer equivalent; blackouts; continued drinking despite health problems; drinking of non-beverage alcohol (i.e., sterno, hair tonic).

B. Impairment of social or occupational functioning due to violence, poor social skills.

C. Duration of this condition for at least a month.

2. *Alcohol Dependence*

A. All of the above in addition to the development of a tolerance or increased ability to metabolize alcohol, and withdrawal symptoms if alcohol is abruptly stopped. The above definitions need not all be satisfied and in fact any one of the above qualifies the individual psychiatrically as an alcoholic (American Psychiatric Association, 1980).

The medical and mental health fields see the flaws in this definition. All agree that it is a "disease". Many see the distinction between the two types as spurious and irrelevant. Many see the attempt to get away from the term "alcoholic" in favor of a less pejorative term as unnecessarily fearful of giving offence (Ryan, 1990).

A Closer Look

The Brentwood experience is that although all of the above criteria are satisfied by some clients, and some criteria satisfied by other clients, there are individuals from alcoholic family origins and other chaotic child-rearing environments who do not satisfy any of the above criteria. Unlike the major mental disorders where we often see very abnormal individuals coming from normal homes, the alcoholic invariably comes from an environment of chaos and disorder. These individuals make up a disproportionate number of mental health workers and medical professionals. They do have, however, the same thinking, emotional and behavioural patterns as the "drinking alcoholic", differing only in the consumption factor. Alcohol consumption, although the most visible behaviour of the alcoholic, is not the *sine qua non* of alcoholism. Witness the burgeoning interest in the Adult Child of an Alcoholic Syndrome (ACOA). Many of these individuals are teetotalers but are clearly saddled with behavioural patterns similar to their alcoholic parents. What is the common thread? (Ryan, 1990). There are several:

1. Instability and inconsistency of the self-concept secondary to the failure of the developmental environment to foster adequate development of this personality feature at the appropriate milestones. This is a failure to develop a stable sense of self as a person and as a member of a family and a member of society at large. A poorly developed sense of connectedness to others. A sense of being different from others, a sense of having to act "as if" they were normal. Many of our clients date this experience to their earliest years.

2.   Emotional instability, moodiness, feelings of anger, isolation, despair that seem to come out of nowhere and are not solidly connected to life events.

3.   Narrow and inflexible problem-solving strategies. The alcoholic jumps at solutions without being able to look at all the alternatives. This leads to poor quality of decision making. This may be more pervasive in the personal life than in occupational areas, although many show this trait in both areas.

4.   Chronic post-traumatic stress responsivity—the tendency to react to life's crises and non-crises in an unpredictable way. Most non-drinking alcoholics show this pattern which appears to get worse rather than better with age (Ryan, 1990).

Clarifying the Brentwood Model of Alcoholism

Throughout recorded history, there have been varied approaches to the definition of alcoholism. It is difficult to achieve any consensus among theorists and practitioners as to the causes or proper treatment of addiction. With the field of addiction merely in its infancy, "clinicians typically have been left to their own devices to develop and adopt a 'working' model of addiction" (Shaffer, Kauffman, p. 230).

Fr. Paul developed a viable model of alcoholism and recovery from his extensive sharing in the pain and suffering of those afflicted. At a very early stage, he discovered a common spirit among alcoholics and a genuine sense of community as they ventured together towards sobriety, and a holistic recovery. Unknown to him at the time, he had initiated, much like Jean Vanier with the handicapped, a community which in essence was reflective of the message of the Gospel—a message of Good News and hope for alcoholics who had lost their way (Clarke, 1974).

When Fr. Paul originally became interested in working with the alcoholic, he was frustrated because he couldn't reach the "drunk" solely by himself. Finally, Fr. Paul met a man who had been twenty-five years in recovery and in desperation asked him: "I can't get through to so and so, would you talk to this practicing alcoholic and to his family?" When the recovering alcoholic came in, he called the practicing alcoholic an SOB. The practicing alcoholic took this confrontation and did not so much as wince. This was a revealing insight for Fr. Paul. This is the point at which Fr. Paul was able to get out of the way and allow one "drunk" to heal the other "drunk" (Devin, Gallant, p. 21). Recovering alcoholics can risk themselves with the alcoholic who is in pain and they can be very acutely aware of what such a person needs, physically, emotionally, intellectually and spiritually.

The recovering alcoholic in the Brentwood program does what O.W. Mowrer (1971) espouses of mutual self-help groups—they foster honesty, responsibility and involvement with the distraught alcoholic who feels lost and alienated (Mehr, 1980, p. 197). This is the model for which

Brentwood claims its success and continues to be its fundamental, spiritual, healing principle. Gerald Caplan maintains:

> *   Followers of the human services approach to people problems support mutual self-help groups and reject the notion that only highly educated and specially trained professionals from the traditional disciplines of medicine, psychology, and social work can effectively help others. (Mehr, 1980, p. 185)   *

As ironic as it may appear, Fr. Paul was searching for a deeper meaning and purpose in his own life and in the process he found an overpowering source of peace and fulfillment in "being there" for the alcoholic. Having been rooted in an alcoholic family himself, he was painfully aware how he himself had been ravaged by a dysfunctional family condition. He too had to unravel his own sense of disturbance, hostility, rebellion, turmoil and agitation with life. He found his strength and courage in ministering to his fellow alcoholics. As Fr. Paul observed in his initial involvement with the alcoholic:

> *   The pie-in-the-sky type of God, devoid of people, always disturbed me. When I would speak with parishioners, either in the rectory or in their homes, I knew that this type of limited and superficial contact was not sufficient. Because their hurt and pain was so severe and because they had been so totally devastated with intolerable experiences of life, they required a continuous longterm follow-up. This required a support system like we have here at Brentwood.
>
> It was very difficult for me in the beginning to shed outdated values which I had inherited either from home, school, the church or even the seminary and just "be myself." Some tasks were impossible to accomplish within a parish context. Something was required which would renew people's lives and it had to be done by someone who could command leadership and who would not be afraid to veer from what was given to him. Charity House with its growing pains was a beginning and it eventually evolved into the Brentwood program we have today.
>
> I took ordinary people, people who didn't have "an axe to grind" to help me establish this new way of recovery. I had to assert my authority so that the mission would not be undermined. I made no bones about who was in charge and this was readily accepted by those who knew what I was attempting to accomplish. They had to trust me and they had to carry out the mandates which made the program work.   *

Some people do not want to be honest about the fact that their lives are in shambles or in total disarray. They would rather live a lie. Some just go through the motions, all the while refusing to grow and "let go". Brentwood provides an opportunity to challenge people about their deceptions and to render them more accountable to themselves and the people close to them. In Fr. Paul's words:

> ✳   There is no question about it. Being in touch with God and in touch with reality is one and the same thing. This fundamental Brentwood premise is opposite to what the world glibly thinks and certainly is opposite to the life of the alcoholic, which is both out of touch with God and out of touch with reality. It has to be more than just words. It has to be a *living-trusting-experience and encounter with God in and through other people.*   ✳

Clarification of the Brentwood Model

Brentwood appreciates the complexity of diverse variables which must be considered when dealing with addicted individuals. Fr. Paul strongly believes that "alcoholism" or addiction as we know it today is primarily based on misplaced and misdirected pseudo needs. The need for love, caring and sharing, intimacy, work, play, family, relations and so on became a misplaced obsession for lust, inordinate power, control, sexual prowess, workaholism, seduction, family dysfunction and pseudo relationships. Alcoholics build their whole lives on a false foundation. It is a fragile base built on sand where nothing solid can take root. As seen in Table 1, to the alcoholic or the addict, love becomes seductive lust, caring becomes unbridled power, sharing becomes control and intimacy becomes sexual prowess. Table 1 shows a dialectical process which encompasses the alcoholic's positive and negative life dimensions. Unless trust is established, alcoholics live in a world of fantasy and emptiness. By risking responsible encounters with others, alcoholics provide the opportunity for play, work, caring, sharing, love and intimacy. It is in the very act of reaching out to others that alcoholics can experience inner peace and freedom. It is in the depth of genuine relationships that they can bring together the richness of both past and future into living fully in the present. They no longer need to be markedly preoccupied with the past or anxiously fearful of the future. They can be reasonably comfortable in the present moment without the excessively neurotic need to escape from reality.

The Brentwood formulation of alcoholism came into existence at a time when alcoholism was not clearly defined and when the issue was not as widespread and as highly researched as it is today. "A scant quarter of a century ago alcohol problems were virtually neglected" (Pattison, Sobell, Sobell, 1977, p. 1). The Brentwood formulation was intended to meet an urgent need and to establish the fundamental basis of the disease as it was observed from the countless people who came for help. The word "alcoholic" at Brentwood began as a mere expression: "Oh, you're alcoholic," and was intended to express the distortion of reality in the alcoholic's mode of *thinking, feeling* and *behaviour*. It included cross-addiction as well as multiple addictions. At the time, the term "alcoholic" was used to include what Ann Schaef refers to as "ingestive addictions" as well as "process addictions" (1989, p. 2).

Just as Schaef (1989) asks; "Isn't the co-sex addict also an addict, be it sexual, romance or relationship?" (p. 6), the parallel question can also be raised, "Isn't the co-alcoholic also an alcoholic in the sense that that person portrays or exhibits all the traits and characteristics of the alcoholic with the exception of the substance ingestion?" Brentwood has helped alcoholics, drug abusers, multiple abusers, sexual abusers, wife abusers, children abusers, co-alcoholics, co-dependents, para-alcoholics, relationship addicts, food addicts, gambling addicts and criminal offenders. There are people from all of the above categories who have testified to the impact of Brentwood upon their lives. Fr. Paul does not harbor any doubts as to his treatment model for recovery because he has woven his interpretation of alcoholism through the sensitivity and insights of his own experience with the alcoholic. It is unique in that it touches the fundamental values of a person's life such as truth, justice, charity, faith, hope, love, kindness, forgiveness, prudence, fortitude and temperance. "During the early part of this century, the church yielded primary responsibility for the promulgation of values and the regulation of values and regulation of individual conduct to the state" (Shaffer, Kauffman, p. 231). Though Brentwood emphasizes moral responsibility for individual action, it also recognizes defects in character as well as social and emotional immaturity.

Further Implications of the Brentwood Definition

"Traditional concepts of alcoholism are closely tied to the common-sense understanding of the term 'addiction'" (Pattison, Sobell, Sobell, 1977, p. 31). All existing definitions of alcoholism include the condition of ingestion of alcohol. Clinicians are not in agreement as to

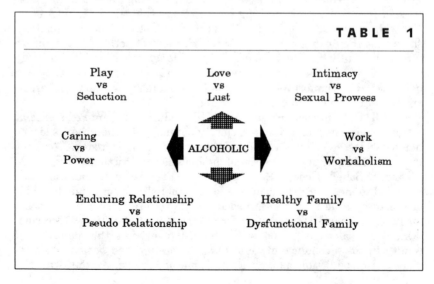

TABLE 1

Play vs Seduction	Love vs Lust	Intimacy vs Sexual Prowess
Caring vs Power	ALCOHOLIC	Work vs Workaholism
Enduring Relationship vs Pseudo Relationship		Healthy Family vs Dysfunctional Family

what other categories should go into the defining conditions. Brentwood's definition of alcoholism is used generically to include any and all addictive thinking, feeling and behaviour which renders a person's life unmanageable and incapacitated to carry out the normal duties and responsibilities. To paraphrase and add to Clinebell's (1984) definition of alcoholism and to capture the substantive definition of the disease one can say: A person is an alcoholic if one or more of his major adjustments in living—health, vocational, social, or marital—is periodically or continuously hampered by alcoholic thinking, alcoholic feelings or alcoholic behaviour. Brentwood infuses the notion that alcoholism does not necessarily require the ingestion of a drug. Alcohol is a self-defeating solution to a spiritual problem. Stanton Peele (1975) advocates the need to expand our conception of addiction if it is to become a viable concept. Addicts are perpetual emotional invalids who are driven by intrapersonal and interpersonal fear. They perceive life as a constant threat to them. Peele proposes from a social-psychological point of view a reformulation of the term addiction taking into consideration the subjective experience of the addict to his perception, his feeling and his reaction to the significant elements in his environment. In these terms then, an addiction exists when a person's attachment to a sensation, an object, or another person is such as to lessen her or his appreciation of and ability to deal with other things in her or his environment, or in herself or himself, so that she or he has become increasingly dependent on that experience as her or his only source of gratification.

Etiology: Early Roots in Childhood

Brentwood considers the etiology of the disease of alcoholism as stemming from very early in the individual's social, psychological and spiritual development. According to the Brentwood philosophy, each alcoholic is hurt, wounded or seriously offended at an early age, carries this resentment, turmoil and confusion into later years and adopts a dysfunctional approach to life, people, situations and events. They are spiritually stunted in their growth, emotionally crippled, behaviourally maladapted and cognitively disoriented, disorganized and disturbed. There are numerous influential factors which dispose a person well before taking the first drink or the first attempt at drugs. Environmental factors also have a strong impact on the individual's addictive pattern of maintenance.

Even though a good number of individuals are classified as "alcoholic" in the Brentwood sense of the term, it does not mean that they will go on to the point where actual consumption is a serious problem. The latest Brentwood statistics indicate that 95 per cent of those who seek admission have a substance abuse problem. But it has become very evident at Brentwood that many people who have never taken to drinking or drugs have the same characteristics as alcoholics; they develop the same alcoholic thinking, have the same alcoholic-type feelings and display the same disruptive behavior. More of these people are coming into the Brentwood recovery program for help. This is happening because more and more people in the community—including some from the helping professions—have become aware of the successful holistic healing power of the Brentwood support group system.

Very early in life the alcoholic personality refuses to love, is closed to people and lives in fantasy as an escape from reality. The alcoholic refuses to grow. As early as seven to eight years of age, the alcoholic, it is believed, has made up his/her mind not to listen to anyone. At this early stage, he/she becomes distrusting, rebellious and hostile. A child is well on her way to being alcoholic before the teen years. Children of alcoholic families are compelled to live by unwritten codes where they cannot appear weak in front of others. They are already embarrassed by the alcoholic parent and cannot tolerate any further humiliation (Devin, Gallant).

The whole Brentwood definition of alcoholism is predicated upon both an assumption of abuse and a continuum of inception and includes:

1. Early Tension

2. Dissatisfaction with Life

3. Family Discord and Disharmony

4. Problems in Living

5. Distortion in Thinking, Attitude and Behaviour

6. Poor Self-Image

7. Faulty Defense Mechanism

8. Association with Negatively Influencing Peer

At an early age, children with alcoholic personalities have more or less developed a predetermined mind-set and have already preoccupied themselves with being self-centred and self-serving. They have made up their minds: "No one, but no one, is ever going to get close to me. I will never share a feeling. I will never share an emotion." In hostility and rebellion, the young alcoholic says:

> ✴   *Come on world, come on. I'll take you on! I don't need anybody! I never will! Anytime I let anyone get close to me, they hurt me and there's no way that I'm going to be hurt, and there's no way that I'm going to show my feelings or my weaknesses. And no one will ever embarrass me again.* (Devin, Gallant, p. 4)   ✴

A Closed Heart

The young alcoholic, with a closed heart, fears rejection and as a result chooses to live in fear and isolation from others. They either attempt to overachieve in order to meet false expectations or procrastinate to avoid failure. But they do not have a *drinking problem* as much as they have a *people problem*. Brentwood considers the *heart* to be the primary issue. As one Brentwood participant aptly remarked: "Alcoholism is a cardiac disease; it is a problem of a closed heart" (Selby, 1989). For the most part, the alcoholic personality is incapable of giving or receiving love, is out of touch with reality, is blind to other people's feelings and is unable to shut off the mind from negative self-talk. According to Brentwood, the question which has profound implications for the helping professionals is fundamentally a spiritual question which is both *intra*personal and *inter*personal:

> How does one reach the heart of the alcoholic person? How does one exercise the heart? Do you reach it simply with the proper nutrition? Do you reach it simply with physical exercise? Any one of these approaches would be ineffective and would be doomed to failure because these tactics, by themselves, would be incapable of reaching the alcoholic person. If someone has been unable to love from the time he/she was fourteen years old, what has to happen in his/her life in order for him or her to become a more complete person again? (Devin, Gallant, p. 9)

The Brentwood term "alcoholic" was considered as descriptive rather than a formal definition of the disease and was not originally intended for scientific scrutiny from other segments of the helping professions. The Brentwood model of recovery would be very plainly seen in some circles as unorthodox. The fact that the Brentwood model does work is attested to by the countless number of people who have achieved sobriety and who are living rich and productive lives as a result of the treatment which they received from the program. There are countless active alumni who volunteer their time and effort in order to bring peace and sobriety to the new people on program. The revealing paradox of the spiritual dimension of twelve-step self-help groups and Brentwood is that it takes a recovering alcoholic, not merely a professional, to help and heal another alcoholic.

Mehr (1980) points out that peer therapy is effective because the significant other people are well-motivated to help the alcoholic in need to change; they are linked into the psychosocial need system of the alcoholic and they function as important role models for them. This approach, according to Mehr, has powerful implications in terms of producing effective therapeutic change and in terms of being extremely cost-effective. The helping professions must realize that the "drunk" loves the other "drunk" and because she does, a rebirth occurs and the person is given the opportunity to become more complete and whole again (Devin, Gallant). Analogous to a mother's pain of childbirth, a recovering alcoholic knows the pain and struggle of another alcoholic. Wegscheider, (1981) who quotes Virginia Satir, states: "For lasting recovery, the alcoholic must become more than sober; he [she] must become whole" (p. 11). Satir maintains that through a holistic treatment program which treats the whole family and the whole person of each family member, each one is offered recovery and continuing growth to realize her potential growth. This requires that those who are working with the alcoholic and their families must be pursuing their own personal development. At Brentwood, the struggling alcoholic goes to the other alcoholic who is attempting to grow and maintain sobriety. The alcoholic is not afraid to open up her heart to the other "drunk". The alcoholic can become more transparent because with the enhanced self-worth and confidence the heart becomes alive, it feels and wants to gravitate toward people. For the first time in her life, the alcoholic is able to participate in a structured environment—she is able to be "part of " a family. Romeder (1982) speaks of fraternity as a common denominator that links members together: "On the individual level, fraternity is one of the basic human needs, like the need to belong (to a community, a race, country, class party or other group) or the need for affiliation" (p. 11).

Brentwood works through a dynamic interactive system of values, goals and relationships which is developed in greater detail in Chapters 3–4. The addiction-prone individual now substitutes her previously defeating patterns of behaviour with newly acquired ones. The individual learns to get "high" naturally in and through other people. However, it realizes that remembering one's former ways and patterns is extremely disturbing especially when it confronts the person's resistant self-will, and seeks to support the alcoholic for as long as is necessary.

According to Brentwood, the alcoholic's life was in shambles long before the actual drinking became a noticeable problem. By the time the alcoholic gets to Brentwood, she feels like a "nobody". A significant percentage of those who come to Brentwood have admitted that they were close to suicide and many have either tried it in some form or they have had an urge to try it. Some have spent their lives going to bed at night feeling that they wanted to die and all the while fearful of death itself. Some have been afraid to keep their eyes closed because their heads would not stop spinning and the alcohol was not breaking the destructive pattern, or it was not bringing them into reality. Their fantasies were driving them insane (Devin, Gallant).

Brentwood places a strong emphasis upon the importance of family. Frank Goble (1970) speaks of the success of a self-help program for drug addicts, which has some similarities to the Brentwood program. The members find themselves with a group that acts as brother, sister, father and mother. The group cares about each individual. The new member gradually learns to accept and abide by the rules and schedules, and to accept more and more responsibility for his [her] own life.

The Brentwood model is directed precisely at the core of most addictions. Brentwood provides an opportunity for alcoholics to come to grips with the most pressing existential questions; "How can I conform to the irrefutable and fundamental laws of God and nature and thus live in harmony with myself and others? Kurtz (1981) would undoubtedly argue that through involvement in such a program as Brentwood, people come to grips with their distorted sense of idolatry.

The alcoholic gains an understanding of the paradox that escapes most people—that is, that we delude ourselves into believing that we are near-gods seeking perfection, and in maintaining this delusion we are forever destined to frustration. (Toresen, Budd, 1981, p. 174)

Those who have gone through the Brentwood program realize that the program does not demand pristine purity or perfection but they accept the fact that certain fundamental processes of peace and serenity are assured in their lives by living one day at a time in a spirit of love, forgiveness and compassion.

The Brentwood formulation of alcoholism is indeed a unique one. Considering the Brentwood concept of alcoholism, it is possible for some to: (1) not drink at all, or (2) drink in socially acceptable ways and still be deemed a "full-fledged" alcoholic with all the characteristics of an alcoholic except the excessive use of alcohol (Table 2).

Brentwood's Objective Determinant of an Alcoholic Condition

As shown in Table 3, Brentwood uses objective criteria in determining the nature of the alcoholic condition. It looks at the barriers to spiritual growth and development and the surface elements which

---

TABLE 2

The Brentwood Diagnostic Framework
Thinking, Attitude and Behaviour

Range of Thinking, Feeling & Behaviour	Age Stage Tolerance	Diagnostic Threshold	Barriers to Spiritual Recovery
Pre-Alcoholic State	Age 5–12	Attitude problem	Mistrust, negativity
Alcoholic State	Age 13–16	Closed, defiant	Actual ingestion
Post-Alcoholic Stage (Substance)	Age 17–65	Rebellious	Product of alcoholic or addictive home
Post-Alcoholic Stage (No Substance)	Age 17–65	Despondent	Product of alcoholic or addictive home
Transformation One to Ten Years	A new lease on life	Happiness, peace, joy	Spiritual transformation, actualization

render an individual incapable of joy, peace and fulfillment. Schaef (1989) quotes Charlotte Eliza Kasl in saying what Brentwood holds as a fundamental truth and principle of alcoholism, addiction and substance abuse: "Addiction is, essentially, a spiritual breakdown, a journey away from the truth into emotional blindness and death" (p. 10).

Determining Who is Alcoholic

Brentwood determines if an individual is "alcoholic" by a careful examination of the following questions (Table 4). Some of these points have been modified from Clinebell's questions: "Are you an alcoholic?" (p. 21).

Indicators	TABLE 3
Closed	Blind
Unloving	Rebellious
Seclusive/Insular	Ungrateful/Unappreciative
Self-pity	Uncaring/Destructive
Negative/Angry, Hostile	Driven/Compulsive
Disengaged/Disinterested	Excessive Mood Swing
Work Problems	Argumentative
Intolerant	Dejected
Fantasy/Daydreaming	Prejudiced
Self-will	Special
Barriers	Poor Judgement
Misplaced Priorities	Falling Apart
Dominant Egotism	Non-Conformity
Reaction Formation	Non-Compliance
Domineering	Controlling
Self-righteous	Breakdown
Dishonest/Deceptive	Vindictive
Unreasonable/Impracticable	Defiant
Unbelieving/Skeptical	Frightened
Impatient	Fearful
Lonely	Disheartened
Surfacy/Superficial	Shallow
Phoney	Artificial
Emotionally Crippled	Guilt-ridden
Sorrowful	Suicidal
Greedy	Compulsive
Hurt	Wounded
Self-centred/Egocentric	Immature
Arrogant/Inconsiderate	Rigid

TABLE   4

1. Are you closed to people in your life?
2. Are you unable to love fully?
3. Are you unhappy because of your disposition?
4. Is your behaviour affecting your reputation?
5. Have you ever felt remorse following your negative attitude or destructive behaviour towards others?
6. Do you frequent company who weaken your spiritual life?
7. Does your behaviour make you careless or reckless with your family's welfare?
8. Do you have very little ambition or motivation?
9. Do you have difficulty sleeping?
10. Are you constantly guilt-ridden?
11. Do you spend a great deal of time alone?
12. Has your physician treated you for some type of psychosomatic illness?
13. Do you lack self-confidence?
14. Are you dissatisfied with your home life?
15. Do you have an endless preoccupation with self?
16. Do you do stupid things which have grave consequences to you, your family, your friends, or your work?
17. Do you have moments of deep despair and hopelessness?
18. Are you dissatisfied with your work life?
19. Do you feel incompetent?
20. Is your thinking consistently biased, prejudiced and disturbed?
21. Do you frequently find yourself alone and desolate?
22. Do you exhibit a tendency to be disengaged and disinterested in the events and activities in your life?
23. Are you seen as unreliable and undependable?
24. Do you spend most of your time in remorse and self-pity?
25. Do you inflict psychological or emotional pain onto people who are close to you?
26. Have you had a poor and damaging childhood?
27. Do you treat others with disdain and disrespect?
28. Is your behaviour towards others vindictive and calculating?
29. Is your life riddled with insecurity and indecision?
30. Do you feel imprisoned with worry and turmoil?
31. Are you unable to concentrate or work effectively?
32. Are you super-sensitive and super-critical about people and things?
33. Do you have a tendency to be obstinate and rebellious?
34. Did you live by punitive and unwritten laws at home?
35. Do you feel like you want to "take on the world"?
36. Are you afraid of people and situations and go out of your way to deliberately avoid people?
37. Are you like a walking time bomb constantly on the "muscle"?
38. Do you drain other people of their energy and resourcefulness by your negative attitude and disposition?
39. Do you feel rejected and despised (as if others don't want you)?
40. Are you cunning and manipulative in your behaviour towards others?

Addiction

Brentwood's Perception of Addiction

Having considered Brentwood's perception of alcoholism, we will now go on to look at its perception of addiction, beginning with the topic of dependence.

Dependence

Dependence refers to a series of behavioural, physiological, and psychological disturbances which occur on abrupt withdrawal after alcohol has been administered for a prolonged period of time (Cicero, 1980). According to the Physician's Manual of the Addiction Research Foundation, (1981) *psychological* dependence is a:

> psychic drive for a feeling of satisfaction that requires periodic or continuous administration of the drug to produce a desired effect or to avoid discomfort...physical dependence is a physiological state of adaptation to a drug, normally following the development of tolerance, which results in a characteristic set of withdrawal symptoms (often called the 'abstinence syndrome') when administration of the drug is stopped. (Bratter and Forrest, p. 140)

According to Jaffe (1975), there is a compulsive urge, distinguished by an overpowering involvement with the use of a drug and a high proclivity to relapse after withdrawal. Peele (1985) maintains that since addiction takes place with a range of objects, there is no item which is inherently addictive but rather it is owing to a combination of social, cultural, situational, personality, and developmental factors. Therefore, addiction as a multifactorial phenomenon occurs along a continuum, in various stages, and is not confined to a single object. In order to evaluate the degree of addiction within a person, it is necessary to assess the span of addictive possibilities in a person's life. How harmful is the involvement to the individual? Does it limit other sources of gratification? Does the individual perceive the involvement as essential to his or her functioning? Does the involvement upset the person's overall social, psychological and physical system?

Similarities between Alcoholism and Addiction

According to Peele (1985), alcohol is one drug whose equivocal relationship to current conceptions of addiction has muddled the study of substance abuse. Nikken (1988) maintains that addiction has mostly been limited to the context of alcohol and drug use. Nonetheless, there are millions of addicts who have never used mood-altering drugs to experience euphoria. There are a multitude of people addicted to food, gambling, relationships, nicotine, caffeine, religion, anxiety, sex, shoplifting, work, spending, and many other forms of enslavement. There are countless other people who are barely subsisting because, in quiet desperation, they are living lives of "emotional isolation, shame, and despair caused by their own brands of addiction" (Nikken, p. 1). Since addiction is no longer related solely to alcohol and drugs, Peele (1975) suggests that we look at the whole range of objects, endeavors, and even people to which we become addicted.

Schaef (1987) maintains that individuals who function within an addictive system exhibit the same alcoholic thinking ("stinkin' thinkin'") in terms of dishonesty, self-centredness, dependency and the need for control although they are not abusing alcohol or drugs. Nikken has produced a definition of addiction which is a variation of the one in the chemical dependency field: "Addiction is a pathological love and trust relationship with an object or event" (p. 10). Since addicts substitute sick relationships with events or processes for healthy relationships with others, their relationship with a mood-altering "experience" becomes central to their lives (Carnes, 1983). Addiction is an aberration of the natural: what is normal loses all its luster. According to Carnes, addictive individuals progressively seek people and objects for abnormal gains to the exclusion of reality. When family, friends and work are no longer a priority, addicts retreat from them. To maintain their addiction, they need more of the same—a compulsive urge to use, at their own expense and at the expense of others. According to Carnes, addiction permeates the most rudimentary of human processes and alters creative life-giving energy into a destructive, demoralizing compulsivity which diminishes the addict's *values and relationships.*

No "Quick Fix" or Easy Solution

Just as so many things in life are not what they seem to be on the surface, the same is true for substance addictions, process addictions, relationship problems and any other forms of addictive behaviour. Some mistakenly believe that if they can give up this compulsion—this addiction to this or that chemical or to this or that dependency—they will be okay. However, this addictive pattern is much more *complex* than what is seen on the surface since most individuals usually have multiple addictions. It is highly simplistic to think that people can cease addictions by replacing them with so-called positive addictions like running or meditation (Peele, 1985).

According to Bratter and Forrest (1985), to re-establish the quality of their lives, people will have recourse to *self-treatment* but, in the process, will defeatingly resort to compulsive eating, illicit sex, destructive relationships or the use of a variety of drugs. Any alcoholic or addictive system is highly contagious and there are similar dynamics in force for both. The presenting addictive symptoms do not necessarily indicate the cause of substance abuse, nor does the fact that treatment is effective necessarily help to understand etiology. Since excessive substance use has much in common initially with compulsive behaviour in general and appears to derive from many areas of functioning within a person's life, it is necessary to examine the multidimensional nature of the problem by suggesting new and alternative treatment programs (Hart and Stueland, 1979). The finding of factors common to many forms of substance abuse may, for example, have treatment implications for dealing with problems of excessive behaviour in general rather than excessive use of particular substances. With the increasing tendency toward multiple drug abuse, substance abuse should be examined within a more general context of excessive behaviour (Bratter and Forrest, 1985). Excessive use of any substance can be related to such cultural and social factors as peer pressure, availability of the substance, and modeling influences (Gilbert 1976). According to Bratter and Forrest:

> The identification of the number of factors thought to contribute to the excessive use of a substance creates a dilemma for those who are planning treatment. An over-inclusion of variables may provide too little specific information to identify a basis for therapeutic action, whereas focusing on too few variables may ignore other potentially important factors. (p. 35)

Antisocial Personality Types

According to Constance Holden (1985), 25% of the alcoholic population with the character disorder called antisocial personality "tend to be charming, manipulative, attention-seeking, rebellious, impulsive, egocentric and ready abusers of *drugs, other people and themselves*" (p. 168). Psychologist Ralph Tarter maintains that some individuals inherit a behavioural propensity that heightens their risk for becoming alcoholic. Numerous investigators persist in underscoring genetic influences in alcoholism (Schuchit, 1984; Goodwin et al., 1973; Vaillant, 1983; Vaillant and Milofskey, 1982). It has been the Brentwood experience that the person with the alcoholic personality seems to be *born this way*. Some people are born with a predisposed weakness in sight or hearing, some with a weak heart and others with weak kidneys. These people are born with an inherent defect in their system (Gallant, Charbonneau). According to Gorenstein, psychopathic and depressive response styles have also been connected with alcohol issues. The psychopathic style is unable to anticipate and evade the inimical repercussions of behaviour as in the consequences of overdrinking. The depressive style, with the discomfort of negative affect, invariably wavers towards sustained alcohol intake for relief (Gorenstein, 1980). "Many personality studies have confirmed that alcohol abuse shows a lack of maturity, impulsivity, antisocial behaviour, or evidence of an inability to cope with life events" (Khantzian, Mack, and Schatzber, 1974; Milkman and Frosch, 1980; Hill, 1980), p. 23. Bratter and Forrest, 1985, quote Khantzian in saying

> ...drug-dependent individuals are predisposed to use and become dependent upon their substances mainly because of severe ego impairment and disturbances in the sense of self. This involves dif-

ficulties with drive and affects defence, self-care, dependency, and need satisfaction. (p. 24)

Barnes (1980) identified the main characteristics of "pre-alcoholic personality" subtypes as individuals who are impulsive, have poor self-esteem, low ego strength, and low social conformity. According to him, the clinical alcoholic personality consistently displays "neuroticism, a weak ego, stimulus augmentation, and field dependence.... Many of the personality traits identifying alcoholics are also common to other psychiatric groups" (Barnes 1979, p. 24, 25).

Skinner, Jackson, and Hoffman (1974) identified eight subtypes of alcoholics using cluster analytic techniques on a bipolar-typal dimension which included: "acute anxiety vs blunted affect, antisocial attitudes vs hypochondriasis, hostile-hallucinative vs neurotic depression, neurotic disorganization vs hostile-paranoid, and emotional instability vs interpersonal conflict and depression," (p. 25). Bratter and Forrest refer to a later study by Skinner, Reed, and Jackson (1976) who

> found that four bipolar subtypes (denial, general anxiety, character disorder, and hypochondriasis) were common among such diverse groups as alcoholics, college students, psychiatric patients, and prison inmates. There is a difficulty, therefore, in using these subtypes to describe an alcoholic personality as distinct from other populations. (p. 25)

Swinson (1980) concluded that genetic factors appear to be a strong etiological influence in men, whereas environmental factors may play a larger part in the etiology of alcoholism in women. Women with drinking problems have more alcoholic first-degree relatives than men (Midanik, 1983). Although maladjustment problems appear frequently in the early histories of both men and women, the expression of this maladjustment is liable to be different. Psychopathology is more common among men with substance abuse, and there appears to be a greater tendency toward neuroticism and depression among women. Women are more likely to have had depressive episodes before the onset of alcohol abuse (Schuckit, 1971). Women who have experienced broken homes before the age of ten are also more likely to become heavier drinkers than men with the same life history, and women also have a greater tendency to relate the onset of heavy drinking to an identified stressful event or situation (Bratter and Forrest, p. 312).

The Basic Need of Love

For people to be happy, to be themselves, to have dignity, self-worth, to be secure and confident within themselves, the basic need is love. The majority, to a greater or lesser degree, are able to accomplish these basic needs reasonably well. But those with an alcoholic personality are powerless to achieve these basic requirements because they are incapacitated in this respect (Gallant, Charbonneau). From a pathological dimension, Nikken speaks to this in drawing a parallel, for example, between addiction and the common characteristics of the uncontrollable multiplication of cancer cells: "The customary process of all addictions is the uncontrollable and aimless searching for wholeness, happiness, and peace through a relationship with an object or event" (1988, p. 4). And according to Peele, when "love" is a distorted means of acting out an interpersonal addiction, it becomes a barren, ingrown dependency relationship with others who are merely commodities for our insecurity. On the opposite end of the spectrum genuine love is powerfully exemplified by a true relatedness and responsiveness to the world. According to Peele:

> The best antidotes to addiction are joy and competence—joy as the capacity to take pleasure in the people, activities, and things that are available to us; competence as the ability to master relevant parts of the environment and the confidence that our actions make a difference for ourselves and others.... Preparing people better to achieve joy and competence offers us our only substantial chance at affecting the incidence of addiction. (1975, p. 157)

The Repeated Inability to Trust

Alcoholics are incapable of believing or trusting the love of their parents. In retaliation, they begin to hurt and offend them. Consequently, at a very early age, as early as eight or nine and certainly at fifteen years of age, there is the negative reacting. This unceasing negativity is much more pronounced than in the normal stage of adolescent rebellion. This is visibly displayed in the young by their excessive opposition, constant disobedience, continual fighting and bickering, endless lying, incessant stealing and physical violence with brothers and sisters. They erroneously believe that people do not understand them. They feel that if people left them alone they would be able to function more effectively. At this point, they mistakenly choose a life of misguided independence (Gallant, Charbonneau). It is an easy step for such youths to move into drug use and deviancy, rebelliousness, alienation, and adolescent behaviour problems, as pointed out by Hundleby (1979):

> Drug use appears to be encouraged by any disruption of the normal child-parent relationships, a lack of involvement in organized groups, or involvement with drug-using peers. Pre-adolescents who begin to smoke are more likely to be low in self-esteem, dislike school, and fear failure (Ahlgren et al., 1982). Motives for beginning heroin use have been identified as pleasure, curiosity, and peer pressure. These motives have been found to change after use, to physiological addiction, pleasure-seeking, and a way of dealing with such unpleasant emotional states as depression, boredom, tension, and loneliness. (Fulmer and Lapidus, 1980, p. 26, 27)

For alcoholics, at a very early age, everything seems to register negatively within their personality structure. They cannot appreciate that their parents really do love them. For example when parents try to give guidance, direction or advice their automatic defensive reaction is to conclude that their parents are against them or that they do not care for them. They unjustly accuse these parents of not understanding them and putting them down and rejecting them: they are unable to see their love, and when parents try to guide and channel them as children, they are blind to this nurturing process. Further, when they are admonished or corrected by their parents, they misinterpret them as being angry at them and they suspect that they only want to hurt them or bring harm to them (Gallant, Charbonneau).

Alcoholics are obsessed with the illusion that they can find love, peace of mind or success on their very own. They disown their parents, their brothers and sisters, their relatives and others close to them. In alienation, they live a guarded and secluded lifestyle or in retaliation they fight with people. Their problem is a "people problem". Nothing seems to work between them and people. Life is the opposite of being smooth: it is rough, hard, frustrating and downright confusing. They end up full of self-pity, hate, fear, resentment and rebellion. No matter what they try, nothing seems to work (Gallant, Charbonneau).

They vacillate from this friend to that friend and gradually their lives turn into "excuse making". Blaming people and finding fault with them becomes more and more exaggerated. Nothing rests easy for them: their life experiences are a constant source of conflict, turmoil and confusion. Unlike ordinary people, they are always dissatisfied, always in search for some kind of peace or happiness that always seems to elude them (Gallant, Charbonneau).

Misplaced Energy

Alcoholics, much like a pampered child, become convinced that if they had their way they could have all the things they want. Instead of acknowledging their own disorientation to life, they accuse other people of being confused. To them, other people are the problem and are the reason why they are not content. This expressed attitude is more than mere words. It is the turmoil and the false innuendos they constantly make about others. The continual fear, confusion and insecurity will simply not shut off. Their fear becomes so strong and overpowering that even normal functions or responsibilities become unbearable, such as meeting people, going shopping or to family reunions. Their fear eventually turns into self-hatred, hatred of others and a dread which leaves them immobilized. To protect their overwhelming fear, they resort to despising themselves, things and other people (Gallant, Charbonneau). Addicts are driven without compromise to inordinately seek an illusive high which is so forceful and rewarding that it becomes both imperative and agonizing. This exacerbating cycle heedlessly perpetuates its own existence and, as a result, addicts alter any authentic feelings which remain and, in the process, abandon all practical coping efforts. With their emotional lives out of control, the addictive experience becomes the core of their self-concepts (Peele, 1985).

Distortion of Self

For alcoholics, self-pity is not simply another word but a defeatingly stagnant force which renders them impotent to act in the ordinary affairs of life. They are out of control and unable to function effectively. Their thinking is distorted and they no longer experience any sense of freedom or happiness. Faith, trust and obedience are no longer meaningful to them. Their thought capability, their accuracy in judgement, their decision-making ability and their potential for effective action are all clouded and controlled by their excessive negativity (Gallant, Charbonneau). As Nikken describes it, the addictive personality increasingly dominates the person's internal life with a terrible pull in a negative direction and with the byproduct being *shame*. "Shame creates a loss of *self*-respect, *self*-esteem, *self*-confidence, *self*-discipline, *self*-determination, *self*-control, *self*-importance, and *self*-love" (p. 28). According to Chein (1969), the addict, at a very early age "has been systematically educated and trained into incompetence" (p. 23) which renders the individual unable "to arrive at a life vocation and also an inability to achieve desired results from life" (Peele, 1985, p. 121).

No Ordinary High

In the Brentwood sense, it is possible for the "alcoholic" to be an acting-out, vindictive, spiteful "practicing alcoholic" at the age of fifteen years despite the fact that they have not yet started to drink or overindulge in drugs or food. When they discover the "crutch" of drink, drugs, overeating or relationships, whether early or late in life, they succumb to it because it is experienced as an illusive, momentary pleasure which gives them temporary reprieve: one which is fleeting at best. But it is the first experience of a substance which momentarily seems to settle them down and pacify them. Whereas normal people get a high on ordinary things in life and can feel elated being with other people, seeing a good movie, going to a game or visiting a friend, this is not so for the most part with alcoholics (Gallant, Charbonneau).

Life for alcoholics is plagued with confusion, frustration, emptiness and boredom with people. The fleeting pleasurable sensation of alcohol, drugs, gambling, overeating or using people as objects for their own gain provides the high which they never otherwise experience. But these momentary pleasures cannot be sustained. Yet, like everyone else, they need to feel good: to feel a *natural high* which alcohol, drugs, gambling and overeating cannot give them. And anyone who steps in the alcoholic's way of getting this *illusive* high is seen as an enemy whom they must war against (Gallant, Charbonneau).

The underlying longing and insatiable quest of alcoholics is for them to be *loved* for people are by nature made for happiness. They yearn to have peace of mind, to feel contentment and to experience joy in their lives. This basic need has been placed in them by God. There is no amount of alcohol, drugs, gambling, food or object relationship that will fulfill or satiate this intense yearning alcoholics have for the "good life" which God has instilled within them (Gallant, Charbonneau).

Spiritual Hibernation

To be deceived into believing that the addiction or the compulsion is primarily the alcohol, the drugs or the food, is to miss the whole point. All these various types of addiction are seen in the Brentwood philosophy as a spiritual disease. Alcoholics are not able to relate normally with others or be at ease with people because they are not a significant *"part of"* any nurturing or sustaining relationship. Essentially, alcoholics are in "spiritual hibernation"—their spirits are anesthetized to those around them. Having dulled themselves to their own inner spirit, it is impossible for them to get in touch with the spirit of others: they cannot enter any meaningful dialogue. This is why Brentwood advocates that it is essential to have a spiritual recovery program as opposed to a more or less narrow and restrictive alcohol, drug or food-control program. To do otherwise, is to miss the key spiritual ingredient to recovery: it means treating the symptom and not the cause and dealing with the surface issues and not the core issue which is essentially *spiritual* (Gallant, Charbonneau).

The Journey Needed for Recovery

The Brentwood mission is to assist those in recovery in their long and strenuous journey towards developing their normal abilities to live effectively. This is accomplished in and through other people. Each person on program becomes "family" for others. It is believed that this same caring and sharing process must be continued and sustained if any long-term gain in sobriety or spiritual recovery is expected, and unless alcoholics continue this fellowship and sense of shared community where the giving and receiving of support is experienced, they invariably return to their previous stage of selfishness. As Nikken states:

> Once an addictive personality is developed, the active addict or recovering addict will always see the world in a different perspective. Like any other major illness, addiction is an experience that changes people in permanent ways. This is why it's so important that people in recovery attend Twelve-Step and other self-help meetings on a regular basis; the addictive logic remains deep inside of them and looks for an opportunity to reassert itself in the same or different form. Recovering addicts continue to go to meetings and work the program because they continue to be addicts. Recovery is the continued acceptance of addiction and the continuous monitoring of the addictive personality in whatever form it may take. (p. 18)

Many of them, without the sustained support and reassurance of the other alcoholic, eventually return to alcohol, drugs, gambling, overeating or seductive relationships. At best, they settle for being "dry drunks" refusing to deal with their underlying addictive issues. They act much the same as they did when they were in their disease: they sever themselves in their addictive process from healthy nurturing relationships and merely regress to other false forms of dependency and isolation. Nikken quotes such a person: "I now find myself eating for all the same reasons I drank: I'm lonely, I'm afraid" (p. 25). Another addiction impedes any deeper dimension of peace or serenity in their lives. According to Nikken, for recovery to occur, the addict must break the *addictive relationship within the self.* In Table 5, Stanton Peele has devised five questions to determine the seriousness of an addictive habit. The more one answers "yes" to these questions as to the meaning of a habit, the more pronounced is the addictive issue.

A Sense of Victory

Society has a great deal of leverage on the lives of alcoholics and the issues they contend with each day. It is becoming increasingly aware that recovery is possible and is earnestly intent and willing to understand and aid those people who are afflicted with the disease. The members of society can now understand and support those who are addicted to alcohol, drugs, gambling, food and relationships, whether it be their own parents, brothers or sisters, spouses, children or friends. They can help alcoholics in their struggle to conquer this disease and they can assist them in becoming healthier members of their families, their

---

TABLE 5

Are You Addicted?

---

1. *Erase negative feelings (pain, anxiety and despair).* Does your habit make you forget your problems? Do you indulge most when you feel worst?

2. *Detract from other involvement.* Does your habit harm other aspects of your life? Does it prevent you from fulfilling other responsibilities, trying new experiences, dealing with people who don't share the habit?

3. *Artificially prop up self-esteem.* Must you return to your habit regularly to feel okay about yourself and your world? And do you feel bad again when you stop?

4. *Routinize your life.* Do you refuse to vary the routines surrounding your habit? Do you ignore all changes in your life circumstances while pursuing it?

5. *Are ultimately not pleasureable.* Do you enjoy your habit less and less with time? Can you skip it when you don't even anticipate enjoying it? Do you continue mostly because the thought of not doing it horrifies you? (Peele, p. 181)

work and their community. Recovering alcoholics can achieve victory
not only over the addiction to a substitute but, more importantly, they
can achieve a sense of victory and accomplishment with life itself
(Gallant, Charbonneau). Stanton Peele recommends:

> The steps out of addiction, therefore, are: to find a superior alter-
> native to the habit you want to break; find people who can help
> you puncture your complacent defenses; change whatever you need
> to in your life to accommodate your new, healthier habits; celebrate
> your new, nonaddicted image whenever you can. (Rucker & Rucker,
> 1989, p. 183)

According to Peele (1985), addicts can give up self-defeating rewards when they uncover superior fulfillment in family and other significant features of the environment in which they carry out their
everyday activities.

Some people come to Brentwood at a time when there is very
little to live for. Brentwood claims that its most striking successes have
been achieved because people share a common tragedy, a similar type
of suffering. This, of course, it has in common with A.A. and other self-
help groups, but it makes such community building absolutely central
to its program. By alleviating their more pressing problems, Brentwood
gives them an opportunity to develop a more positive attitude toward
their problems. People lend support to one another and in the process
develop a sense of achievement and a sense of gratitude for being able
to "be there" for one another in their pain. Life takes on a powerfully
new dimension where it can be lived and faced more maturely.

The Brentwood model has been applied to a large number of
alcoholics, substance abusers, and addiction-prone individuals and has
strong claims of success. Some of these success stories are identified
throughout. To quote the present Auxiliary Bishop of the Diocese of
London: "The fruits of Brentwood are evident in the community. When
I spoke to people on my parish visits, I was amazed at how many had
been helped by Brentwood. Their lives have been touched in a very real
and meaningful way."

CHAPTER 2

Brentwood: A Shared Community[1]

This chapter will first speak in general of the shared community model which exists at Brentwood, pointing out the main features, its spiritual aspect and authoritarian stance, which distinguish it from other models. We will next consider the Brentwood perspective and the demands it makes on residents. Next, we will look at the Brentwood practice with its support system of residents caring for one another, Father Paul's daily input of talks, the daily scheduled life, the therapeutic community in action, the supportive process; and finally, the confrontation process.

A Community-Oriented Recovery Program

Over the last twenty-five years Brentwood has developed a *model community* and *recovery program*, which is both spiritual and therapeutic, for people who suffer from broken spirits, instability and addiction. Brentwood's ultimate goal is to restore the *physical, emotional, psychological, spiritual* and *social* dimensions of a person's life-situation. It encourages individuals to relate to God in and through other people. Residents are taught certain basic principles which permit them to turn their lives around in a manner that is *individually productive* and *socially responsible*. The Brentwood program provides an avenue by which wounded people can honestly examine the primary issues which are at risk in their lives and act constructively upon them. They are taught how to love again and to open their hearts to the experience of other people by getting in touch with their own inner journey.

Brentwood's *spiritual* dimension encompasses a cosmic, ecumenical and Judeo\Christian perspective. This approach is utilized for all residents regardless of their social, economic, racial, cultural, educa-

---

1.   The author is indebted to George DeLeon for his insightful Chapter on "Therapeutic Communities for Addictions" from which the author modelled the organization and structure for presenting this Brentwood Profile.

tional, professional or religious background. It is designed to awaken in people those dormant qualities of hope, trust, joy, respect, caring, compassion and forgiveness which have been anesthetized because of their spiritual blindness and their inability to love. According to Fr. Paul, being spiritual means living according to nature and being in the right relationship with oneself, with others and with God. It means "people needing people". It has everything to do with treating people with respect and giving them the dignity they deserve as human beings (Gallant, Charbonneau). The spiritual is a *"life-filled way of living"*; it implies choosing a personal path which is filled with the wonder, energy and excitement of the Spirit and which at the same time is *"radically communitarian"* where we share the pain and struggles of others on our way (Fox, 1991). Those who are afflicted with the wounds of alcoholism, addiction and substance abuse are craving for *spiritual affection* and *spiritual communion* with others.

The *therapeutic* dimension of the program utilizes the power of a healing community, thus addressing what Brentwood considers the primary cause of addiction—spiritual escape from the *truth* and *reality* of life. In this approach we see a congruence with the definition of community put forth by Scott Peck (1987), as:

> ...a group of individuals who have learned how to communicate honestly with each other, whose relationships go deeper than their masks of composure, and who have developed some significant commitment to "rejoice together, mourn together," and to "delight in each other and make others' conditions our own". (p. 59)

McMahon and Campbell (1967) also see community as authentic interpersonal relationships where real human experiences are shared and individuals can reveal themselves as they really are. As opposed to a superficial exercise of getting acquainted, people in community are genuinely open to one another in a way that makes an authentic encounter possible. Community at Brentwood is promoted through a dialogue of acceptance and self-disclosure by means of a responsive environment where love is personified through intensive *caring, sharing* and *confrontation*. Though each person is encouraged to discover and enhance his or her own uniqueness, they are also urged to discover a common ground of interdependence, which breaks down the walls of loneliness and isolation and moves them into the action phases of recovery, thereby learning to assert their own "best selves" in the process. Here, through a genuine dialogue of acceptance and self-disclosure, community happens. To paraphrase MacMahon and Campbell, the Brentwood community grows because people listen to and accept themselves as they really are, give themselves as they truthfully are to the needs of others, create the environment for real human experiences and share their struggle with one another.

The Difference

Brentwood can be distinguished from other alcohol and drug treatment facilities by several essential factors. *First*, the primary teacher and therapist is Fr. Paul Charbonneau who, through his own vision of communitarian life, developed its philosophy and its approach to community. For many years he was alone in the counselling role since there was no one else to help him. Only recently have trained staff been available to take on leadership and counselling roles which they are now able to share with him. *Secondly*, the "spiritual community" is a necessary, central and effective medium of therapeutic intervention. This stems from Brentwood's definition of alcoholism (Chapter 1). The substance abuse or addiction of choice is seen as a coverup to dodge the root cause of residents' enormous distress: spiritual blindness and emptiness, the inability to love and the refusal to forgive themselves and others. Residents are held accountable for themselves and others close to them. It involves *people needing people*, for their own growth and development. This calls for a spiritual transformation of their character to enable them to discover paths out of the "mess" they have made of their world. The Brentwood program, as previously mentioned, evolved from the direct practice of involving the "other drunk" in healing the alcoholic rather than from the practice of utilizing professional intervention. It was based on bringing together two people who cared—*one* who was in the process of recovery and knew the pain and anxiety associated with the addictive process and the irreparable damage it caused family and friends, and the other who wanted, perhaps hesitantly, a *new way of life*.

A *third* factor consists of residents and group leaders who act as living role models and who, through caring confrontation, engender change in the process of recovery. Up to the time of their coming on program, they found themselves defenseless in their distorted way of thinking, their overwhelming emotional response and their ineffectual behaviours which had rendered their lives barren and futile. *Fourthly*, there is a professional staff who deal with the normal everyday individual problems of people on a regular and consistent basis. *Fifthly*, the cost of treatment is less than thirty dollars per day per person making Brentwood by far the least expensive of any effective recovery home.

Spiritual Community

It is difficult for residents to deal with the deep wounds caused by their addiction. As we have already pointed out, addictive people have suffered severe trauma in their *past* relationships, are unable to deal effectively in the *present* in their interactions with others and fear there are no viable prospects for the *future*. However, when they experience extreme pain and struggle on their difficult journey to recovery, they are lifted up by a *"power greater than themselves"*, the spiritual strength which, in and through other people, is at the center of the Brentwood experience: Brentwood offers a spirituality for the "here and now". For most, this presents a problem because many are distrustful about religion or family as a result of their addictions. The Brentwood program is in accord with McMahon and Campbell (1967) when they say:

> For example, if my relationship with my human father was not a warm and accepting relationship, then I find it difficult to discover and relate to God the Father as warm and accepting. I transfer my human experience over to my relations with an unexperienced God. Ultimately, I project my experiences with an earthly father onto God, and end up by relating to him as I do to my own parent. (p. 10)

At Brentwood, God's "self-communication" is seen as taking place in and through a shared community: personal dialogue with God is in and through one another. People are joined together in a spirit of unity that makes personal growth and fulfillment possible. This is in accord with the view in McMahon and Campbell that it is in the very relatedness with one another that people receive their *self-identity*. This comes through the gift of selfless love, and through responding to each other's need through self-sacrificing generosity, wherein they discover the experience of oneness within the "family of God". To again paraphrase McMahon and Campbell, Brentwood people experience a community whose deepest cohesive bond is that of a selfless love, inexplicable on the basis of human resources alone in its transforming power and effects. The core concept of its program is the recognition that this power of union is not *exclusively* person-made but "God-inspired" and "God-directed". A loving community such as Brentwood, which prevails in harmony, accord and solidarity, is a living witness of a force which surmounts the capabilities of its members. It is only by being fused to the power of selfless love, through *agape*, that members of the fellowship can abide within such an intrinsic bond, selflessly devoted to the service of one another. Brentwood stands as a living testimony to an authentic caring and "spiritual" community which in turn bears witness to the power of *agape* in its members. This living testimony has been a rich source for enhancing the self-identity and personal growth of its members. Brentwood transcends rules and regulations and stands as a commitment to a person, namely Fr. Paul, and to a way of life which is "God-centered" and "people-oriented".

The Brentwood spirit calls people to celebrate their differences and transcend their own uniqueness by committing themselves wholeheartedly to the healing of each other's wounds. The term *"Brentwood spirit"* is experienced as *"life-giving"*. In a spirit of faith, trust and love, a community celebrates a common bond which uplifts them and brings out the best in each. The genuine pride which people take in their own sense of fulfillment is extended to their families, their relatives and to the workplace.

Therapeutic Community

Although Brentwood accommodates a vast spectrum of addictive personalities, almost 95% of residents have been either abusers of drugs and/or alcohol, and in addition often have numerous other addictions. The majority of residents (about 75%) are male, and the remainder (25%) are women. The ages vary from 14 to 70. While the majority of residents come from parents with substance abuse, some are from homes with other prevailing addictions and in some cases have been physically and sexually abusive and/or have themselves been abused. A number of residents suffer from immature, obsessive-compulsive or anti-social-type personalities. Most have been in trouble with their families, their work, and/or with the law.

At Brentwood, there can be found the eight curative elements of a "therapeutic" community which Hollidge (1980) suggests are necessary: (1) Instilling of Hope, (2) Feelings of Togetherness, (3) Altruism, (4) Socialization, (5) Development of Interpersonal Skills and Sharing Information, (6) Group Cohesion, (7) Reliving Situations From the Family of Origin and (8) Identification. Residents of Brentwood have reported a tremendous sense of promise for themselves through the closeness and the genuine concern and caring confrontation they have experienced from others. Because they can acknowledge their own *self-worth* and recognize their *sense of value to others*, they have a more ardent desire to belong, to be part of and to make their contribution to the strengthening of the group process. By becoming honest with their past and by forming new friendships and allegiances with other residents, they come to an awareness of a more productive way of life.

The Brentwood Perspective

Brentwood grew from a small group of two or three to a much larger community. Most residents, in one way or another, have basically failed to abide by the laws of God and the laws of nature with the result that the psychological and emotional dimensions of their lives had gotten "out of sync". Such people, it is believed, suffer from more than a physical addiction or a physiological dependency: it is a functional deficit in their spiritual life—an inability to be honest with themselves and others and a refusal to enter into the lives of others. They live in an existential vacuum which is, for the most part, devoid of a strong moral perspective and they have resorted to alcohol, drugs and other addictions in order to fill the void resulting from their persistent refusal to take mature responsible steps in their lives.

The majority of residents have never learned how to communicate effectively with others and so have accumulated monstrous roadblocks to maturity. Many have been manipulative, seductive and conniving, continuously trying to dominate and control others. Because of this they have been unable to come to an awareness of their deeper needs or make their needs known to others. Others who have enjoyed some degree of affluence which they have rejected, need to learn how to proceed with their lives in a manner which brings them peace with others.

Since Brentwood sees the underlying cause of alcoholism and addiction as self-will, self-pity, self-centeredness and the inability to love, it recognizes that there are predominant characteristics which are similar in all addiction-prone individuals. As a result, all residents are expected to live and participate under the same rules and way of life and to conform, as Brentwood insists: *"ask, listen and do what you're told."* This is deliberately done in order to dismantle their destructive patterns of self-will. Responsible control which is self-enhancing replaces their harmful self-seeking which has sweepingly crushed and obliterated any possibility of their entering into accountable dialogue with significant others. Most residents have been preoccupied with *being right* at the expense of *being loved,* with the inevitable consequence of *spiritual bankruptcy* and *social isolation.*

The Brentwood program instills in residents the ability to think logically and effectively, to feel competent in their unique capacity to care and share and to behave in a fitting manner. Residents are taught certain behaviours to turn their lives around so that they can live individually productive and socially *qualified* lives; that is, they learn to define and accept their own limits and accept the good fortune of others. Only in this way, can they become *"part of"* others.

Through a *"thoughtfully-felt-lived-in experience"*, residents gain an insight into the impediments to growth caused by their addictive disease and begin to recognize a more effective way of life. Once the basics are realized, it becomes increasingly more natural for the alcoholic to do *God's will* instead of self-will, to *live for others* instead of being preoccupied with self-centeredness and to *live in conviction, determination,* and *confidence* as opposed to self-pity and remorse. When they are in possession of these enriching attributes in their lives, they carefully begin to experience a "natural high", *in and through other people.* In this way, their former habit of substance abuse or their addictive proclivities are diminished because of the tremendous influence that these positive forces have on their behaviour.

Requirements for Entering Brentwood

As part of the Brentwood experience, Fr. Paul provides specific talks which offer strategic links in drawing people together. The resulting *"in-faith-community"* is then able to celebrate pain and suffering, and openly acknowledge the need for one another. By entering into the anguish and despair of each other's lives, residents are able to recognize the dialectic between *sadness* and *joy, love* and *hate, peace* and *anger, darkness* and *light, weakness* and *strength, death* and *life.* By embracing both sides of the human condition, people are brought to a fullness of life which makes celebration and rejoicing possible.

There are certain basic prerequisites which are necessary in order for a person to enter the Brentwood experience. In order for the

Brentwood experience to be effective, it requires (1) residents who have a strong *incentive* for recovery, (2) the sense of a shared community through the experience of strong relationships, (3) people on program who can model for the residents a new life-style and (4) a program which provides spiritual intensity and relevance.

✳ *Incentive*

In order to overcome their disease, individuals must have the strength and fortitude to undergo dramatic changes in their way of *thinking, feeling and being in the world* and must come to realize positive pulls which directly attack the heart of the disease. They must come to realize that external positive forces are a great deal less painful and more bearable than the previous internal pressures which they have needlessly weathered in the past. The program is geared to deal with resistance, to discern any hasty withdrawal from the program and to bolster the level of participation and contribution in the recovery process.

✳ *Relationships*

Addicted persons invariably cut themselves off from mature, mutually enhancing relationships with others as they attempt to hide their real selves from others. Now they need to accept the challenge of personal and interpersonal growth. At Brentwood this is accomplished in and through the fellowship—those on program and the alumni who return faithfully to give to the new and old residents. It is this forceful and dynamic influence which allows them to come to grips with the still unresolved issues in their lives and to permit the healing process to take root.

✳ *Modelling*

Since the residents need other people, it is imperative that they learn to model the preferred behaviour of those who have dramatically modified their former lifestyle and who are living happy and constructive lives. Since their behaviours occurred within a social context, it is necessary that they learn, unlearn and relearn within a healthy social environment—a "spiritual" and "therapeutic" community. The leaders are models and friends to the residents who, through example and verbal expression, provide them with a more practical way to deal with their everyday issues.

✳ *Intensity*

The recovery process is itself therapeutic and has an overriding influence upon each resident. In a brief period of three months, the residents must compensate for an ineffectual past and must prepare themselves for a life of renewed energy and vitality. The structure of the program prevents as much as possible any damaging and disruptive interference from the outside until each person is able to establish a balance within themselves, one which prepares them for living in the world "out there". The significance of Fr. Paul's daily talks, the intensity of the day-to-day activity with its emphasis on "one-day-at-a-time", the hour-to-hour confrontation of honesty and the minute-to-minute reality of staying in the *now* are powerful incentives for turning one's will over to a *Greater Power*. The Brentwood program is not for the faint-hearted, the mediocre or the sluggard, but for those who are prepared to make a substantial commitment in terms of time, effort and energy.

The Framework of The Brentwood Practice

As leader, Fr. Paul determines the pace and sets the tone for the whole Brentwood experience. The rationale for this strong stance stems from his own personal style of leadership and his belief that if one leaves authority *solely* in the hands of residents the results can be devastatingly irresponsible. While keeping close rein on the overall operation, he skillfully delegates duties and responsibilities to staff and alumni who together with the residents comprise the Brentwood community. Staff persons direct the everyday activities under the influence of Fr. Paul.

In addition to the staff, who are required to deal with meals, maintenance and administration, a large part of the work is done voluntarily by the residents, under the direction of the group leaders. Work assignments are allocated by group leaders and by senior residents on program. There are no preferences as to job choice and anyone can be assigned to peeling potatoes or to lavatory tasks. Whether a resident happens to be a doctor, an engineer, a lawyer or other professional, each can be assigned what would appear to some as "menial" tasks since there is no preferential status when it comes to this disease. Moreover, there is a therapeutic dimension involved wherein residents must learn to submit voluntarily to the will of properly qualified persons in authority. Consequently, it is an integral part of each person's program that they be encouraged to volunteer for whatever work that authority considers best for them at that moment as this serves to reduce the dominance of self-will.

✳ *Social Support*

Obviously, as Brownell and Shumaker (1984) have pointed out, there are not too many, if any, people who can live effectively under pressure, with its resulting tension and turmoil, unless they have close ties with others. The use of support groups has met with a great deal of success in the area of alcohol treatment. Members of Brentwood have been seen by Edmonds (1989) to undergo "an intensive residency program where the changes are said to be significant" (p. 26).

Although many researchers have shown in a positive vein that social support enables people to live their lives more productively, others have claimed that a social support group can itself become a crutch, an addiction, which a person cannot live without (Bruhn & Phillips, 1984; Albrecht & Alderman, 1987; Jurick, 1987). Edmonds points out that:

> Some scholars would argue that a person who does not let go of a
> social support group is no different than a kidney patient who has

to return to the hospital for dialysis treatments. Just as kidney patients are dependent on the dialysis machine, alcoholics are dependent on the support group for their well-being. (p. 27)

The Brentwood program has wisely taken this danger seriously, realizing that no one institution can be the sole support of any person. It therefore seeks to rehabilitate persons who have been devastated by their disease by a slow process assisting them gradually to enter into and cope with the wider community in which they must live. It seeks to help them break out of their blind wilfulness so that they can experience the joy and support of the Brentwood community and later that of mature persons in the "real world". As they slowly begin to mature themselves, through a somewhat long and arduous process, they are taught and helped to discern people in the wider community who will be supportive. They are also taught how they too can become helpful to people who themselves need support in their growth towards health and wholeness.

With residents living in such close proximity to one another, it is inevitable that the effectiveness of the therapeutic community is exercised in large measure in and through them. They are the key figures in disseminating the Brentwood message among the fellowship in the one-on-ones, the groups, the alumni meetings, on their jobs, in their rooms and during their social and recreational hours.

The emotional and psychological rapport which is developed between the group leaders and the residents fosters a spirit of *people helping one another*. They oversee the performance of each resident and report to Fr. Paul and the clinical staff any person whom they feel needs specific attention. The chief clinical psychologist offers insights to the group leaders on how to foster the growth of specific residents.

※ *The Social Support of Senior Residents*
Most of the senior residents become imbued with the Brentwood philosophy. These are residents who are "walking" the values and beliefs of recovery and are able to instill in the newer residents Brentwood's purpose and function. This whole process is *awe inspiring* to the new residents who want to get in on the action. In so doing they develop a deeper meaning of community. They then begin to feel "part of " as opposed to "against" or "isolated". The senior residents encourage them to participate and contribute. They introduce them to the other residents and sometimes direct them to have a one-on-one with someone who has encountered similar problems. This realization of a "mutually shared experience" reduces the anxiety of a resident in difficulty because such a person knows that they are not alone in their predicament. The all-pervasive "ripple effect" has an enormous impact upon their sense of connectedness and belonging. As the new residents move into their ninth or tenth week, they are then prepared to take on the role of senior resident to pass the "message" again to the new residents. It is this repeated influence which engenders such allegiance and loyalty to the spirit of recovery through personal and interpersonal growth and witness.

Most senior residents see to it that the new residents comply with the rules and regulations necessary for the safe operation of the facility and though they show a reasonable degree of empathy and warmth towards the newer residents, they are not afraid to confront them when they see them doing something which is not in keeping with the spirit of recovery. If the new residents have a poor attitude or if they are lacking in motivation, most senior residents will approach them and question them about their disposition. It is the overall positive impact which each person has upon the other which seems to leave a lasting mark on the whole fellowship. This is reflective of a true community spirit. By a total sense of giving to the spirit of community, the residents feel a freedom within themselves which they never quite grasped before. They can now reap the benefits of their journey into recovery and it just feels so good that they have a strong desire to *"pass it on"*.

Fr. Paul's Daily Talks: People Needing People

Fr. Paul's talks are a powerful medium for achieving the basic goals of recovery and for enhancing the spirit of community. The talks basically maintain that people are children of God and have within them the capacity to choose a better way of life, progressing from bondage to freedom. This occurs *in* and *through* other people, since the greatest need of people is love and caring, to love and be loved, to care and be cared for, to forgive and genuinely feel forgiven. This means PEOPLE NEEDING PEOPLE and is God's plan for our well-being and happiness. I have outlined some of the main elements which characterize the dynamic process of recovery through the theme expression of Brentwood: PEOPLE NEEDING PEOPLE. The following provides a brief glance of Fr. Paul's basic message of recovery as exemplified in his actual talks at Brentwood.

P   *Problem recognition and resolution*
E   *Experiencing the need for other people*
O   *Open to confiding, consulting and accepting direction*
P   *Positioning oneself to listen to others and their concerns*
L   *Learning to think, feel and behave responsibly*
E   *Expression of self in an other-directed manner*

N   *Needs of the individual being met: The spiritual*
E   *Examining the language of the heart and the emotions*
E   *Emotional balance, security and confidence*
D   *Discipline and responsibility*
I   *Internalizing mature adult values*
N   *Needs distinguished from wants*
G   *Gratitude for a valued growth experience*

P   *Participating meaningfully in the life of family
     and community*

E *Enhanced energy level and zest for life*
O *"One with" the self and "one with" others: A must*
P *Peace, forgiveness and joy*
L *Love, understanding and patience*
E *Enhanced cooperation and socialization*

P. *Problem recognition and resolution*

Each resident must remove the blindness which impedes the recognition of problems. Residents have been blind to the fact that for true happiness to be experienced such qualities as trust, faith, honesty and forgiveness are essential prerequisites. Fear and insecurity causes them to falsely protect themselves by pretense, excuses, lies, procrastination and self-destruction. It is this blinding control which keeps them confined to a narrow world which eludes problem identification. They see the world through rose-colored glasses and with a distorted perception which debilitates their focus on reality and the here-and-now. It is here at Brentwood that the other recovering alcoholic can help peel away the hardened layers of selfishness, excuse-making, self-pity and denial.

E. *Experiencing the need for other people*

Previously, some residents have lived a morbid, isolated and stagnant existence devoid of meaningful interaction with other people. They have failed to admit that their greatest need is *to love* and *be loved.* Unable to care or share, nurture or be nurtured, they defy their own nature as human beings. By failing to bring peace and joy to others, they remain sad, lonely and desperate. They have developed an "I don't care" attitude. They have become powerless to allow others to be part of their lives. At Brentwood they learn to invest themselves in the lives of other people. Nothing is to be held back if they want to be healed from the shackles of the disease. This means surrendering to the love and care of others and also being sensitive to their needs.

O. *Open to confiding, consulting and accepting direction*

Residents, for the most part, have been preoccupied in self-indulgence, driven by unbridled impulses and compulsions. Their behaviour has been illogical and incomprehensible. As a consequence, they have become loners, isolates and rejects.

Brentwood can help when residents are willing to follow the direction which is set down for their own benefit. Through acceptance and self-disclosure, residents come to acknowledge both their strengths and weaknesses and to enter into genuine dialogue and community with others where they can share their hurt and their pain. Residents come to realize that by asking, listening, and doing what they are told, they can begin to see that *obedience* and *direction-taking* are the ways in which they can gradually begin to accept responsibility for themselves. This means respecting the needs of others and cooperating with the wishes of other people. At Brentwood direction is provided so that residents can get their lives in order by identifying their priorities and by constructively handling their indecisiveness.

P. *Positioning oneself to listen to others and to their concerns*
The word *interest* has the connotation of enthusiasm, eagerness, concern, curiosity and ambition, where one is attracted, intrigued and "turned on" by people and events in life and away from the morbid preoccupation of self—*Me! Me! Me!* Only by listening attentively to the pain of others are residents able to heal one another's wounds. People can truly celebrate their differences by committing themselves wholeheartedly to the needs and concerns of others. The lives of most residents have been replete with boredom, frustration, depression, misery and despair. Life for them has been tedious, dreary, dull, sterile and monotonous. As opposed to interested, or enthusiastic, they have become heartless, and their lives have become devoid of meaning. To be able to listen to others, it is important for residents to pay close attention to them and to be open to their communication.

Though Brentwood teaches residents the need to be "*concerned for*", to be "*involved with*" and to "*feel with*" in their listening to the heart of the other person, by the same token, residents have to allow others to listen to their story and allow them to be concerned for them also. They can now, in turn, trust the concern and interest which others have for them. By open listening and caring, residents can be interested and genuinely responsive to the hopes and aspirations of other people, making their lives richer and more invigorating.

L. *Learning to think, feel and behave responsibly*
Unbridled fantasy is an escape from being responsible. Residents have exclaimed in the past: "I can live my own life and nobody has the right to interfere or say anything. I am only hurting myself." But their irresponsible actions have caused severe harm to others. Residents need to guide their lives by principles which allow them to be more fully human and more fully alive. By living responsibly they are able to sustain their own growth and provide a mature and productive environment for others. Brentwood offers an alternative to self-destructive patterns of behaviour and holds residents and the fellowship accountable for that behaviour.

E. *Expression of self in an other-directed manner*
Most residents have always been preoccupied with their own selfishness and egocentricity. They wanted to be entitled to *exceptions* and *exemptions*. They felt that they never had to do anything for anybody but that others should serve them hand and foot. They despised being seen as ordinary, common people. They considered themselves to be "self-made" and of a "special breed" with few people as talented and gifted as they were. They had appointed themselves instant experts on everything. In effect, they became lonely and isolated "misfits" who desperately felt that they did not belong. The only distinction they could lay

claim to was that they were specialists in self-pity bored by their own misery and detachment from others.

Brentwood teaches each person to enter into the world of others and to open dialogue with them. This prevents further isolation and provides the opportunity for the genuine sharing of the self. This process breaks the vicious cycle which renders residents unable to look beyond the narrow confines of the "imprisoned self." They can reach out where love and acceptance is possible. Now they learn to care and share and open themselves up to the needs and concerns of others.

N. *Needs of the individual being met: The spiritual*

All residents have a need for acceptance by others but whenever it was offered to them in the past, they vehemently refused it. The self-pity, the negativity, the anger and turmoil have acted as a wet blanket which crushingly prevented them from meeting their most basic needs. Instead they catered to misdirected pseudo-needs. The need for *love, caring, sharing, intimacy, work, play, family*, and *relationships* becomes a misplaced obsession with *lust, inordinate power, control, sexual prowess, workaholism, seduction, family dysfunction* and *pseudo-relationships*. To the alcoholic or the addict, love became seductive lust, caring became unbridled power, sharing became control and intimacy became sexual prowess. Brentwood provides an opportunity for people to restructure the quality of their lives and exchange *reality* for *fantasy, openness* for *closedness, courage* for *fear* and *love* for *hatred*.

All residents have an inherent need for love, security, self-worth, self-fulfillment and confidence. God provides people with what is needed day by day. Defeat and discouragement are experienced when one confuses needs and wants. However, recovering alcoholics can risk themselves with the other alcoholic who is in pain and they can be acutely aware of what such a person needs physically, emotionally, intellectually and spiritually. Brentwood exposes the residents to what they need in life and shows them the necessary steps to take to achieve their basic needs.

E. *Examining the language of the heart and the emotions*

Residents have a "people problem". They have built an iron-clad wall to block the emotions of the heart and have chosen to live in fear, rejection and isolation. They have lost the ability to distinguish pain from pleasure, right from wrong, joy from sadness, honesty from dishonesty and courage from fear. Some people do not want to be honest about how their lives are in shambles and in total disarray—they would rather live in dishonesty. Some simply go through the motions, all the while refusing to grow.

Brentwood provides an opportunity to challenge people about their deceptions and to render them more accountable to themselves and to the people who are close to them. The heart needs other people in order to blossom and be fully alive. "I will give you a new heart and place a new spirit within you taking from your bodies your stony hearts and giving you natural hearts" (Ezekiel 36: 25–27).

E.   *Emotional balance, security and confidence*

Most residents have paid the price for not being flexible and adaptable. They are unable to distinguish their true feelings and emotions because they have buried them so deeply within. With fear, insecurity, confusion and doubt, there is no balance. Some have gone to the extreme of wanting evil to happen to others if this meant that "good" (as they perceive it) would happen to them. They always lived life in opposite extremes, painfully crushed and afflicted.

The first steps to growth and maturity call for a caring and understanding heart. By responding to the unlimited challenges of life, residents are provided with a stability and equilibrium in their lives. A balance is fostered by learning to relax, changing their pace, and being open rather than closed to new ideas and possibilities.

D.   *Discipline and responsibility*

Some residents have never been able to surrender self-will to God's will. Since they have spent the majority of time *doing their own thing* at the expense of others, they have never developed the discipline essential to live at a mature adult level of development. They have conformed to their own weaknesses and distortions and in the process have become more or less "undisciplined". They mistakenly thought that it was just natural to have love and they did not think that they had to work "for it" or "at it". Life had become so desperate that they did not have the discipline to make even minor decisions on their own. They did not even realize that it took discipline. Ironically, in their own undisciplined fashion, they demanded independence for themselves and subservience from others, particularly their spouses. But the last thing residents require is licence to do as they please, since they have unsuccessfully done this all their lives. It is presumed that they have come to Brentwood to gain insight into personal and social responsibility and therefore must develop discipline and accountability.

I.   *Internalizing mature adult values*

In the past, most residents had refused to "grow up". For them fantasy was an escape from accepting adult responsibility. Their irresponsible actions would cause severe harm not only to themselves but to others. They were inconsiderate and unreliable in their daily affairs and they lacked consistency and dependability. This imbalance led to intolerable frustration and deepening mistrust between themselves and others. In fact, they became so exclusive that their own families finally did not want anything to do with them: they saw them as incompetent and domineering.

Residents have come to Brentwood because they were "fed up" with their immaturity and their fraudulent lifestyle. Lying, deceitfulness and self-deception were decoys used to "con" themselves and others. They were blind to what was right and good for themselves and for others.

N. *Needs distinguished from wants*
Invariably in the past some residents have vacillated aimlessly with no purposeful direction. They did not know what was meant by the need to be loved and accepted, to be responsible, to be happy or to be "part of." They did not know the difference between basic needs and wants. Consequently, some did not know what values to pursue, what direction to take or what the real purpose of life and living entailed. They simply were never taught. By being responsible and accountable, they fostered within themselves the ability to experience wisdom and fortitude. But wisdom comes only as the result of their being able to experience love, and, is the ability to know and to do what is right, what is good and what is necessary for their own benefit and the good of others.

Their basic need is for a here-and-now-honesty. When the need to trust, understand and forgive others is ingrained in their lives, they develop the discipline necessary to care for others physically, emotionally, psychologically, socially and spiritually. They become more qualified, not only to meet their own basic needs, but capable of knowing what will fulfill the basic needs of other significant people in their lives. Satisfying basic needs provides a boost to their self-worth and to their peace of mind. They become more prudent with their choices and more creative in their endeavors.

G. *Gratitude for a valued growth experience*
Their previous ingratitude caused residents to hold back from others, to cherish nagging self-doubt, to indulge in negative self-talk, to still demand things in their own childish way, to refuse to give up their obstinate self-will and to try very consciously and persistently to control and dominate people, places and situations. With a very selfish attitude, they had strings attached to all their demands. The spouse and the children became infected with all their "put-downs" and harshness which was inflicted by them as carriers of this contagious and communicable "dis-ease".

By taking an inventory of the people they have damaged and by opening the avenues of communication, residents are able to develop a bond, a unity and a friendship which makes life worth living. The unconditional acceptance they receive at Brentwood inspires a sense of gratitude within themselves. Residents then become filled with gratitude for this growth experience. They come to appreciate not only their own worth and inner beauty but also that of others. And they become graceful, thankful, grateful, hopeful, and joyful for their new-found experience.

P. *Participating meaningfully in the life of family*
    and community
Most residents in the past were unable to be concerned for others and would not let others care for them. Those on program know the cares and concerns of the new residents because they have "been there". Through Brentwood, residents begin to experience good feelings, their

hearts begin to open with care and acceptance of others. As a result, they become interested and concerned about those close to them. They no longer have to live on the fringe of life and on the outer perimeter of its excitement and challenge. They want to become more actively involved because they realize that Brentwood is family, unity, oneness and fellowship.

E.   *Enhanced energy level and zest for life*
The lives of residents have been filled with apathy and emptiness. In effect, the joy of life had eluded them. They had no more energy or vitality and unless they could have things in their own selfish way, they chose not to be enthused or interested in life or living, thereby diminishing their needed energy for self or others. Brentwood teaches residents how to enjoy life and to come alive again. This happens when they become absorbed in and concerned for the needs and interests of others and when they allow others to meet their needs. Residents can now be "turned on" with a zeal and a gusto for life by being "in tune" with what is meaningful to their spouses, children, parents and significant others, whether at home, at work or in their social lives. Residents realize that they are making progress when they enjoy being around other people.

O.   *"One with" the self and "one with" others: A must*
Residents have never experienced a feeling of oneness or acceptance of themselves or of other people. Instead of a oneness or a bond with self and others, residents have tended to be rebellious, reactive, uncooperative, deceitful and disrespectful. They expected others to have a oneness with them but they refused to have any closeness or unity with others. By "letting go" of their self-ridicule and division within the self and by cooperating with others, they are able to feel an inner connectedness with others. They find this sense of solidarity and wholeness when they can willingly surrender to the unity of the group, the unity of the family, the unity of the workplace and the unity of the community. Such a powerful investment convinces them of their personal sense of belonging and their mutual sense of being connected to something which is greater than themselves.

P.   *Peace, forgiveness and joy*
Previous to their arrival at Brentwood, residents could never forgive themselves for their past life and, therefore, lived in turmoil and confusion: they seldom had any peace or contentment in their lives. Along with this, blaming and ridiculing others permeated their lives to such an extent that they could not forgive others and could not forget the hurts they suffered. Being obsessed with the past simply prevented them from living in the joy and splendor of the present. It merely allowed old wounds to fester and fueled their anger and resentment towards others.
Their Brentwood experience helps them in acknowledging their mistakes, forgiving themselves, coming to understand others who have

damaged them and learning to be compassionate towards them. Peace comes to residents when they begin to respond to the love and needs of others here and now.

L. *Love, understanding and patience*
Before arriving at Brentwood, residents often felt that no one ever understood them, and they rebelled because they felt so desperately misunderstood. This was the result of not accurately perceiving or understanding the thinking, feeling and behaviour of others. Thus, they always misconstrued the motives and actions of others and thought that everyone was against them. And being unable to share their own thinking, feeling and actions, they alienated others further and thus found no time or patience for them.

Brentwood teaches residents to appreciate the total context of other people's communication with them. True understanding entails knowing what their own needs are, what others need and what they attempt to share and communicate with them. It means being able to accurately perceive the integrity and wholeness of others. Brentwood places a major emphasis on the healing of wounds and the forgiving of injuries which calls for an interdependence among people to enter each other's pain and to be there for them. Only by needing others can residents feel love and acceptance in their lives. In proportion as they resist, they push themselves further and further away from forgiveness and love.

E. *Enhanced cooperation and socialization*
Many residents have in the past shown a blatant preoccupation with self. They may have mechanically provided for the family or simply have gone through the motions in terms of their involvement in the community. But they could never be part of the joy or sorrow of others and even refused to allow others into their heart. Brentwood teaches residents to substitute good feelings for bad, by entering into their feelings and moving from self-centeredness to other-centeredness—by reaching out to others. This motivates people to want to be involved with others and to be interested in family and community. They are shown how to be more considerate and how to turn their self-interest into interest for others.

The Brentwood Daily Chronicle of Events
There is a complete schedule of events and a diverse daily regimen to which the residents are subjected. Each resident is awakened at 6:30 in the morning. Breakfast is between 6:30 and 7:30 a.m. Some residents grab a coffee and entertain themselves in a social hour. Some may have things they want to discuss immediately with another resident even before the one-on-ones which begin at 8 a.m. and go to 9:10 a.m. To demonstrate the rigorous demands of the program, no tea or coffee is allowed during these early-morning sessions. This tests the self-will of the residents and encourages them to learn how to comply not only

with authority but with the reality of the world in which they find themselves.

For the time being, the real world and testing ground happens to be Brentwood and the other residents who are on program. This provides for an excellent starting point: if they can *make it here with the constant bombardment of sharing, questioning and caring confrontation*, chances are they will be able to function effectively in the "real" world. After the one-on-ones, the residents have a quick coffee and then join their home groups for forty-five minutes. Each group consists of twenty-seven to thirty members, men with men and women with women. After a ten-minute coffee break, they prepare for the 10:30 meeting which involves Fr. Paul's talk on the topic for the day. At 11:30, the residents break into their home group again to discuss thoughts, feelings, emotions and issues which have surfaced as a result of Fr. Paul's talks.

This is followed by lunch at 12:15 p.m. There is free time until 1:15 p.m. when the residents prepare for the "honesty meeting". Here the residents must acknowledge those attitudes, feelings or behaviours with which they have been deceitful. They must admit the truth to themselves and to the group community. If a resident refuses to be honest, another resident might confront that particular person and invite them to get honest about a certain behaviour which they noticed. This places a demand upon the resident to face up to the real world and to let down their facade. Such an approach reduces game playing and conning which some residents did so well before Brentwood.

There is a short break at 2:15 p.m. Fr. Paul continues on the topic of the day in a one-hour meeting which begins at 2:30 p.m. Following this, the residents are free until 7 p.m. when they attend the alumni meeting. This is followed by a small group meeting which lasts for about forty-five minutes. Around eight or eight-thirty, residents usually gather around tables and engage in small talk, sports, politics or topics of their choice until bedtime which is at 11 p.m. Lights are out and a bed check is conducted at 11:30 p.m. A resident who needs to talk is allowed to remain up after 11:30 p.m. on occasion. Most residents have had more than a full day and normally collapse in healthy exhaustion awaiting another active day.

❋ Consultation

Residents are permitted to seek direction from the counselling staff and from Fr. Paul. They may be having difficulty in respect to home, work or some issue which is leaving them perplexed. Seeking direction is another opportunity for the residents to surrender their self-will and do the will of those who are in authority. These types of encounters encourage residents to attack the very heart of their disease. The aim is not for the residents to achieve perfection but more modestly that they feel a sense of self-worth and personal as well as interpersonal growth. The group leaders each have private cubicles to interview residents as needed. Since the group leaders are looked upon with respect, these sessions have an impact on the residents and are an integral part of the rehabilitation process. Group leaders are able to develop an insight into the personality of each resident and can readily identify trouble spots and issues which are of serious consequence.

✳ *Permissions*

New residents are required to remain at Brentwood during the first two weekends. They may be permitted subsequently to visit their home Saturday afternoon until early Sunday evening. However, depending on the home circumstances, they may only be permitted to receive a family visit on the Brentwood premises or the resident may go home for a Saturday and/or a Sunday afternoon visit. Permission is also required to use the pay phone since they are not automatically entitled to these privileges.

Brentwood is always reasonable when it comes to family needs and such requests are usually given priority. For example, if a spouse is experiencing severe difficulty with the children, a resident may be permitted to help at home between 3:30 and 6:30 and even to remain home for the evening.

Permissions are also granted for time off the Brentwood property between 3:30 and 5 p.m. so that residents can go shopping or attend to business matters. They are usually encouraged, however, to participate fully with the other residents in recreational activities during free time, particularly in their earlier weeks on program. To the extent that residents demonstrate an increasing degree of personal responsibility, they are allowed to exercise more freedom.

✳ *Disciplinary action*

Brentwood has both written and unwritten rules and regulations, conscious of its responsibility for the well-being of each resident and for teaching them how to conduct themselves in their new way of living. Consequently, simple and equitable rules are set up to ensure that no violence is done to any member of the Brentwood community, whether these be physical or verbal threats. Petty thieving is not tolerated nor any sexual relating with another resident. Depending on the severity of the offense, residents may be warned by a staff member or verbally reprimanded by Fr. Paul. Some may be grounded for a weekend or lose afternoon privileges if they display a serious lack of awareness of their disease or lack of motivation to recover. Matters of discipline are usually brought to Fr. Paul, particularly if it involves a serious breach which may demand an immediate dismissal. An example of such a drastic penalty occurs when residents have been drinking or drugging or "fraternizing" with residents of the opposite sex on program. This is deemed to be such a critical incident that it warrants immediate dismissal. Residents may also be asked to leave if, over an extended period of time, they are not showing the willingness or the motivation to apply themselves to the spirit of recovery. Penalties imposed by staff members are reviewed by Fr. Paul and adjusted if necessary. A resident might be required to seek reconciliation for an offence or he or she may have to get honest with the home group or, if the infraction is serious enough, with the whole assembly. Because residents on program need the assurance that they are in a reasonably safe place, Brentwood has to take all the necessary precautions to deter any negative activity which hampers this sense of safety and security.

The Three Phases of the Therapeutic Community in Action

Treatment at Brentwood occurs basically within a three-action phase of recovery—the beginning, middle and the end phase. It is at these varied levels that the staff match the spiritual, emotional and psychological stage of each resident with the intensity of the program. Each resident is monitored by the group leader so as to assess the individual's stress and tolerance level for the rigorous demands of the recovery process. Significant differences among the residents are noted and brought to the attention of the counselling staff. It is in this phase that residents are given the opportunity to choose if they really want to commit themselves to the intensity of the process and if they want to become actively engaged in the healing community.

✳ *Beginning Phase I*

Treatment begins at Brentwood in the acceptance of the new resident as one who has come for help and who shows a willingness to cooperate with the program. Fr. Paul explains: "The beginning phase involves a mutual dialogue of *one alcoholic with another alcoholic* where the honesty, the trust, the openness and the believing can develop in and through the other alcoholic."

The beginning phase is characterized by the fear and apprehension in the newcomers. This can so easily be seen if one took photos of the residents to capture their attitude and disposition from the time they entered on program to their final departure before graduation. Kay Ryan further elucidates the experience for the women when they first arrive on program:

> ✳   It can be pretty scary and overwhelming to be thrown in with all the other people. Some women, when they first arrive, have their eyes sunken. They look depressed and discouraged. Yet within three days one can see a brightness and resilience in their eyes. In most instances, it only takes two or three days. If we could take a picture of a person in the three successive stages: (1) coming in the first day, (2) halfway through the program and then (3) at graduation, we would not be able to recognize that person. Take for example, a new woman on program. At the very beginning, she might look like she has been drawn through a "knot hole". Yet within two or three days of being at Brentwood she is not recognizable because of the remarkable change in her physical appearance. She looks so dramatically different that one can hardly believe it is the same person. She may have showered or done

something to her hair or put on makeup and is now interested in what she looks like. Before she walked through our doors, she had an "I couldn't care less" attitude about herself. Now she appears as if she does prize herself. Even the change in the eyes is so dramatic. The woman is more open and transparent. Often I would encourage the women that if they can "hang in" for two or three days or even a week, they will see the positive results and will want to stay.   ✲

In their initial fear and apprehension, residents are reluctant to become engaged in the process. They resist opening themselves to trust. Before coming to Brentwood, most residents were enslaved in *fantasy* and their lives were devoid of *reality* because they had created immense barriers of fear, hostility, isolation and despair.

The beginning phase of the program for each resident entails the pain, humiliation and embarrassment of having to admit their unresolved predicament and their lack of a sense of *direction*. Appearing half-dead, they realize that they have, as it were, beaten themselves up quite badly physically, psychologically, emotionally and spiritually. Some are barely audible in their communications. They have also, in many cases, severely damaged a host of other people in their lives. For some, there is an overpowering sense of discouragement and hopelessness. A good number of them are so desperate that they have hit rock bottom without knowing *"why"*. They sense a need to belong, but to what? Still, they don't feel *part of* anything. Totally lost and alone, they grope despondently for an *answer*, all the while not even realizing the *question*. Seeing their lives as a total failure and Brentwood as the last straw, they become aware of a profound longing for something more, and move in this direction to achieve it. One alumna recalls her own experience:

✲   I was in terrible shape when I came in. I was suffering from such fear and insecurity. Yet, within hours I felt a glimmer of hope. I got a sense that something good was happening, though I could hardly believe my eyes that it could occur in such a brief period of time. I could not deny the experience and the *"charge of energy"* I received. It was very appealing to see the alumni and to look up to them for what they had. Because they had that peace, I had an overwhelming curiosity to know: *"How did they get this good feeling and this positive attitude towards others?"* My hope was that I would be able to get a little bit of what they had even though it may not have been all that clear to me at the moment.

I got a "taste" for it and I immediately said to myself: *"I want a piece of that."* My whole sense of motivation took a new meaning without my knowing why but simply realizing that I had the *"bug"* for it. I was touched, just ever so briefly, in the first few hours by the depth and profoundness of the program that I wanted more of it.   ✳

The newcomers quite rapidly grasp a sense of hope once they are on program. They begin to understand some of the concepts and are able to accept the Brentwood spirit of recovery. This, in large part, is due to the inspiring support and encouragement which they receive from both the staff, the residents and the alumni who return to share their lives. As the residents settle timidly into the program, and as they work the principles of recovery, they gradually change and start to feel good about themselves. And as they progress, they develop a commensurate pride in the fact that they are beginning to do well.

✳ *Middle Phase II*

In the second phase residents become responsible as regards work and the other obligations which relate to marriage, family and their peers on program. This stage is characterized by their looking and feeling so much better about themselves as they move from a preoccupation with self to an emphasis on *being there* for others. They want to do things for others by reaching out in a more positive way. They have a more positive attitude about family and are asking how they can be more open with their spouse and their children. They are beginning to miss those who are close to them.

Some residents have difficulty in the middle phase because of the complexity of issues they realize need confronting. They may demonstrate either (1) *an apparent air of confidence* or (2) a *genuine conviction* and determination. The staff sensitively detect this sometime cunning and duplicit dimension which could otherwise go undetected.

1.   *An Apparent Air of Confidence*: In terms of overconfidence, there is a danger that some residents might present a false front. It is at this point that the adage "a little *knowledge* is a dangerous thing" can be equally applied to the expression that "a little bit of *sobriety* can be equally devastating." Staff have to guard against a possible sense of "pseudo-recovery" in the residents. Though the person may have gained a beginning degree of comfort and security, the resident can actually project a facade or a semblance of confidence. It could be disastrous for residents to move beyond the middle phase and eventually graduate without having effectively turned their lives around. Having missed this point, these same people could easily relapse.

2.   *A Genuine Conviction*: In terms of personal conviction and determination, residents now realize that they are in the program to get help for themselves and are conscious that if they diligently apply themselves, certain pieces of the puzzle will come together—the self-awareness, the self-worth and the self-reliance. Staff gradually begin to see some changes happening in them, perhaps minor at first, but, nonetheless, significant. There is a

general degree of *"at-ease-ment"* since their beginning recovery is the start of something new.

The middle phase involves a certain "leveling off." Feeling secure and protected from grave and impending harm, they are able to take small risks without fear of total failure or chaos. They are reassured, as it were, that there is a net underneath them to catch them should they falter. They begin to see good things happening to them on program and in the family, both when they communicate on the phone during the week and when they make contact on the weekend. It is safe now for them to come out to gradually and carefully assert themselves. They begin to assume their valid place in the family.

At this stage the residents still have some elements of denial. They begin to feel more comfortable knowing that they belong and they gradually fit into the group in a purposeful way. They establish a sense of trust and a taste of hope—hope to forge ahead and face those aspects which they have been previously avoiding. They now realize that they are accepted and that someone genuinely cares for them. This fortifies their self-worth and enhances their potential. Some, in this middle phase, are able to accept their flaws and character defects and are willing to work on them to improve the quality of their lives. Through caring and sharing with others, their most "confirmed" fears surface and are dealt with forthrightly.

With the insights gained through the inventory process of looking into themselves, the residents gain a flicker of hope and suddenly garner within themselves an increased self-reliance. A certain fear and reservation remains somewhat, because in the self-disclosure, the residents still continue to discover things which they particularly do not want to admit and which they would prefer not to envisage. Residents become terrified in learning the truth about themselves, which, to some, sounds worse than it actually is. It is a very humbling experience for residents to go into inventory while owning their thoughts, their feelings and their actions, something that most of them refused to admit. As one alumnus explains: "For example, I wasn't too pleased with my issues when I started seeing myself for the first time as I really was and the way other people saw me. It was quite a 'downer' for me, as I recall." It is like a person who discovers he or she has cancer but who in fear refuses to take the necessary treatment. Just as the doctor's hands are prevented from helping the patient, so are Brentwood's hands tied because such residents do not allow the fellowship to reach out to them. As they delve more deeply into their written inventory, they are somewhat on a teeter totter, yet on the thrust of a striking breakthrough. It is sometimes, at this very stage, that residents choose to leave because they cannot bear to explore any further their unresolved issues. The residents have to learn to divulge to others those painful areas which they have hidden and which have caused so much aggravation in their lives. Through the process of disclosure, they feel *loved* and *lovable* and are able to let go of the shame and guilt which has surmounted them.

Honesty is what comes through in the middle phase. Although their fears resurface, they are becoming accustomed to the insecurity. And, while learning to overcome it, they are able to enter into a deeper level of self-exploration. It is apparent that their aspirations, their determination and their overall enthusiasm is getting stronger as they proceed. They have a sense of belonging to a family. As one alumna recalls: "For me, it took time to trust because I never trusted anyone. I had my reservations, aware that my disease was still at work." This middle stage is difficult because there isn't anything necessarily *easy* about it. After all, Brentwood did not promise that *it would be easy*; it merely promised that *it would work*. Though perhaps painful, it is in this middle phase that the residents have to "*explore further*". As one person explains:

✻   By the middle phase, we are confronted with the profound reality of our lives and it is shocking and traumatic news to most of us to unravel the truth. In the past, we have always dealt with our crises by means of drugs or alcohol. Now we have to experience the pain first before we can experience the *natural high* which Brentwood provides in and through other people. This requires a discipline which I never exercised before.   ✻

In the middle phase, when residents are working with the honesty, the staff provide the opportunity to delve into the more intense issues. They attempt to draw forth the feelings that caused them such discouragement and despair, mindful of the need to keep the residents on target. One staff member keenly recollects:

✻   Most of us could not define our feelings since we had spent most of our lives avoiding them. We ran away from them. *Fear* and *guilt* are the two feelings which I was able to identify in my experience. I was spinning too much to unscramble much more than those two feelings at the time. I was *all over the place*.   ✻

✻ *End Phase III*

The end phase is, to some extent, a misnomer by the mere fact that people go on learning more about the implications of the disease and more of what it means to practice the principles of sobriety. The key element that has to be ingrained in the residents is that *spiritual recovery* is not just thirteen weeks of sobriety but, more significantly, the Brentwood reality that recovery entails the rest of their lives. Though the formal treatment plan is relegated to thirteen weeks, alumni who remain faithful to the Brentwood principles, feel that they are still in treatment, or better, the "post-treatment" phase: they are essentially in a *continued recovery process*. Now with a more clearly defined focus, theirs is a lifelong progressive journey which does not have to be rushed in a brief period of three months: it is a search that will take a lifetime.

As with life, no one ever completely arrives. The end phase is really the beginning phase of actually *living* this more productive way of life. The process of growth is an endless phenomenon and each day becomes a new beginning. As one staff member realized:

> ✳   I don't think I will ever completely have it—be able to say: "I have finally arrived". If I do, this is the time that I am in trouble because it is at this point that all the elements of the disease come back where I self-righteously deceive myself that I don't need other people, I don't need to trust, *I don't need to confide, I don't need to share the pain and I no longer have to take inventory.* So in one way, it is a good thing that the alcoholic still experiences a certain degree of conflict, dissonance, discontent and feels the need to still accomplish some important goals and objectives in life, that sense of being in touch with reality, acknowledging that one has not completely arrived, lest one begins to falter.   ✳

Actually, the end which is culminated in graduation is simply a conversion from "direct treatment" into the alumni status, where the process of caring and sharing still continues and where a "post-treatment" phase is still essential. Now they realize that they have to go out and practice the principles in the real world and "make it work". Most of the residents are now prepared to go out into the community with their newly acquired tools. If the residents have worked hard in the first and second phase then they should be able to succeed in the third phase, with a true spirit of giving back to the others what they have received. Things then become more and more improved in their lives and they can function with greater ease and contentment.

In terms of sobriety, Brentwood initially provides a "thumbnail" sketch of long-term recovery. The danger is that alcoholics can run wild with a month or so of recovery and can mistakenly believe that they have ultimately "arrived". But if they consider they have become a "success", they will find, as in the past, their lives turned into bitter failure. It is felt that where a good number of people fail is at the point where they get their program going very well in their lives, but then by keeping it exclusively to themselves, become very selfish again. They feel much better but they fail to return it to other alcoholics with the result that they are right back to the selfishness, and thereby lose what they had—the meaning of the whole spirit of life. They might be successful in keeping away from the booze and drugs, because they like what they have and do not want to jeopardize it. But they will not find any joy or happiness at the deeper level—it will merely be going through the motions externally. And sooner or later they will come to a bitter realization that their lives will lose all meaning and will not be worth living. It is therefore most important that they give themselves as a gift to the other alcoholic just as someone had given to them.

Experienced persons become fairly capable of determining whether or not a resident is going to "make it" in the final phase. Residents who have truly applied themselves and have given their "best shot", will be seen to have broken through. They will show a beginning understanding of the principles of life and of the tools necessary to carry on a natural and spiritual journey based on the laws of *God* and the laws of *Nature*. With a renewed enthusiasm and an excitement for living, residents will actually enjoy being alive and be grateful for their new-found freedom. There is an individual transparency which unfolds that is very much visible to other people.

In the last phase, as they are getting ready to leave, residents usually have a great fear about the "outside". In effect, the whole process becomes an adventure. They are, in fact, fearful of what is happening, the unexplainable changes in themselves since they have done so much of the opposite all of their lives. However, by throwing their lives into someone else's hands, their groundless fear of *an anticipated ordeal* is greatly diminished. Responding to one's quest for the more noble and rewarding considerations of life, they become increasingly excited as life takes on so many unrealized possibilities. They are no longer immobilized by their faults and weaknesses. On the contrary, having learned to live with their limitations and to *accept* themselves as they really are, they now have the strength and the courage to accept other people where they are.

The residents' fearful anticipation of leaving begins to spiral as they realize that they now have to initiate this new course of action in the real world. Staff undertake to impart within them a sense of their taking personal responsibility for their thoughts, their feelings and their actions. They have to continue to meet their basic needs and to live a healthier lifestyle each day. The new challenge for them is to courageously live "one-day-at-a-time" and to avoid being unduly preoccupied with either the past or the future. This is something which the residents never did.

In the last stage they are saying to themselves: "*Yeah! This works*" and they get into the other people. Some of the residents have to virtually be held back because they are going *too fast*, still not fully realizing that it takes a lifetime to work on this way of life. The staff find it most rewarding to see this breakthrough. It is remarkable to see the change which has occurred in the lives of residents where their real beauty and self-worth shines forth. People entered the program who had completely given up, figuring that there was no viable way out of their predicament and grew to the point where they regained hope, a sense of self and a sense of celebration in their lives.

The *graduation* symbolizes a noteworthy transition—they leave Brentwood physically but not in spirit, since the graduates will need Brentwood much like a diabetic requires insulin. This is an integral aspect of the continued process of recovery—*people needing people*. The stabilization phase, following graduation is a continued recovery process of one, three, six and seven years: it is not merely the first week to the thirteenth of the actual program.

Implementing the Supportive Process: Walking with the Residents

The supportive process occurs within the fellowship in terms of simply putting into practice the organizing and unifying principles of the program. The result is that residents come to experience an honesty, a caring and a responsibility that is new for them. When they experience this and then practice it for themselves, those on program discover that there is a more viable way to live life fully. Staff provide the major support throughout the three stages of recovery.

The Supportive Process in the Beginning Phase

In the *beginning phase*, the staff deal with the insecurity in the new residents, giving them the support and the confidence necessary. They immediately see the receptionist upon their arrival and are then placed with a senior resident who offers support and guidance in terms of the program and a careful explanation of how it operates. Amidst the consternation, most new residents nonetheless feel a considerable sense of *acceptance* when they walk in the door, whether in the smiling faces, the warm reception, or the honesty and the caring. The new person is treated as prized and valued and is given a tremendous amount of affection and consideration. The newcomers have a sense that the staff and the other people on program accept them no matter what their past life has been like. They usually feel that the staff realize where they are coming from, *who they are and where they have been* regardless of their creed, color or background. Through this process of being understood, they acquire that "dignity and worth" which invariably results from being profoundly "understood" (Curran, 1978, p. 60) and knowing that they are accepted and held in high regard. Not being judged harshly or unjustly, they experience an innate sense of being *accepted* as they are and of being held in high regard as they attempt to maximize their potential. In this way they develop a heartwarming sense of living in a *safe place.*

Newcomers are received with understanding and honesty by the staff, and especially in their home group. Just as staff required the backing when they were on program, they are presently giving it to them. The staff offer them some hope that what has happened to them need not destroy their lives any longer but that they can go on in a renewed way to build a more solid foundation. From the very beginning, new residents are *not alone,* and this warm nurturing experience reduces some of their initial anxiety and apprehension.

From the very first day they feel that there is something meaningful here for them though they may not be fully aware of what it is at the time. No matter what kind of guilt a person may be experiencing (and the majority of residents at this stage of their disease are all feeling some sense of guilt, doubt, or denial), the novices feel that they are speaking to a *real friend* whom they have known for some time. They identify with each other as a "friend, companion" and will soon become confidants with whom they can earnestly communicate. Though the new residents may not be able to speak or say very much, they feel very safe and secure in this home-like environment. They begin to develop, again, a belief in a power greater than themselves.

The staff are able to provide calm for the new residents to the point where they are able to share with the others about themselves. Since the staff and the residents have so many of the same characteristics, they are assured that they don't have to see themselves as weird or as drastically different than anyone else *since each person basically suffers from the same affliction*. The new residents are encouraged to identify increasingly with the others on program through honest sharing. Residents can't help but show gratitude for what is given to them. They all eventually realize that there is something "very special" at Brentwood.

The Supportive Process in the Middle Phase

In the *middle phase* the staff sensitively motivate the residents to a deeper level of self-awareness and in some cases, where necessary, caringly confront them. As they work with the honesty, the staff provide them the opportunity for remaining on target so as to discover what caused them such discouragement and despair. Most residents could not define their feelings since they had spent most of their lives avoiding them. Fear and guilt are the two feelings which are frequently identified in this stage.

To enhance this supportive process, significant others such as parents, spouses and close sympathetic relatives or friends are contacted. They are invited to meetings so that the family disease can be treated in all its aspects throughout the thirteen weeks and beyond.

The Supportive Process in the End Phase

In the *end phase*, the staff attempt to enhance the self-confidence of the residents so that their transparency can come through. At this point, there is a great deal of gratitude on the part of both residents and staff for their investment because they have all worked together in fostering not only the self-worth but also the sense of community which is so essential to the progressive involvement with family and the larger community. The reward for the group leaders and the staff counselors is to see the degree of growth which has transpired in each resident.

The staff have also instilled in residents the need for taking more personal responsibility on their return to their families, their workplace and their respective communities where they can effectively practice living one-day-at-a-time. Meeting their basic needs in and through the fellowship will ensure them a healthier life-style. Since the thirteen weeks is merely the beginning, it is essential that they come back not only for themselves and for the benefits which can accrue to their families but for the sake of new residents and the other alumni who need them.

Confrontation of Staff to Residents

The whole concept of a *"caring confrontation"* goes back to the basic principles which Fr. Paul has taught: "To break the back of self-will, you have to go against the grain and you have to go with the flow." When staff undertake a caring type of confrontation they are accepting this as part of the spiritual work that has to be done to break down the barriers between self and others. Fr. Paul suggests the need to confront and challenge residents to reach out to the person they like the least:

> ✳   An optimum amount of growth can be achieved if people go with an open mind to the resident with whom they think they would have the least common ground and enter into her world. It is believed that their going to someone they don't like or for whom they don't care is the measure of their love for God.   ✳

The basic faults and defects of addictive people are that they have been self-deceptive. The folly of cheating themselves *and others* has been the highlight of the *"con game"*. Confrontation is an invitation to probe the distortions involved in residents' thinking, feeling and behaviour patterns when such patterns "seem to be either self-defeating, harmful to others, or both" (Egan, 1986, p. 219). When new residents arrive on program, staff share about their own previous journey and, in turn, encourage the new residents to share and to self-disclose as their trust in the group leader and the home group increases. The resident might reveal: "I've been fired from my job. I'm living common-law. My marriage is on the rocks." They prod them along in the group, knowing that what is revealed is, usually, only a small part of the hidden "iceberg".

Caring confrontation calls for a delicate balance of knowing when to *prudently confront* and when to *discreetly hold back*, in light of the total context of both the individual and the smooth and efficient functioning of the overall program. But to be effective and meaningful, confrontation has to be used very discreetly. Sharing oneself and helping each resident to become open and trusting is more appropriate than harsh, abrasive or premature confrontation which can sometimes be destructive and counterproductive. No matter what the personality of each resident is, staff usually stay away from actual confronting for the first two or three weeks, partly because some of the residents have so many conflicting issues with which to deal. Confrontation is sometimes done privately on a one-on-one basis where the residents are given a chance to save face and not feel openly demeaned. Staff are able to constructively confront residents in the privacy of their written inventory. This is usually done when staff know that residents are being vague, deceptive or when they are in the "craziness of their disease." It is also done in the honesty meetings or in individual counselling when appropriate. Residents are confronted with the issues relating to their disease. They are challenged when they display an inordinate self-will, a persistent rigidity and a continued lack of willingness to follow the principles of the program. The confrontation is sometimes distressing because, at the time, it may be precisely what is required to bring out the honesty in the residents, though it may not be what the residents *want to hear.*

Most staff have a "gut level" feeling about the residents and they know both *instinctively* and through their own experience in recovery when the time is right to invite residents to speak and when it is *appropriate* to confront them. They also often have a sense of timing as to when it is best to let residents be. As a group leader, one could easily say the wrong thing and "scare them out the door," which in essence might defeat the very objective they are attempting to achieve, namely, *short-term and long-term recovery.* They can tell if residents are too chipper for their own good, too mouthy or too outspoken and in certain circumstances, staff may confront them from the very beginning if it is deemed necessary. Others, momentarily, are too fragile to accept the honesty of the confrontation. The staff, when they themselves were on program, observed this self-defeating behaviour with other residents who required confrontation and are now well-equipped to detect the deception and the "conning" which some attempt to use in a defensive and self-defeating manner. As Gerald Egan states: "Confrontation focuses on the discrepancies, distortions, evasions, games, tricks, excuse-making, and smoke screens in which clients involve themselves and which keep them mired in their problem situation" (1986, p. 220).

Usually staff at first have a brief one-on-one with each new resident without initially attempting to go into any great depth. They may ask them such questions as: "Where would you like to begin? What area might you prefer to concentrate on first? How did you get here? What type of problems are you experiencing? Does your situation involve work problems, court problems or family problems?" Residents are encouraged that if they bear patiently with the staff, with the program and with the other residents, they will begin to see a marked improvement in their overall disposition. This happens naturally as the recovery process unfolds. Once they have briefly allowed the group leader into their world, the staff can then enter again at still deeper levels of awareness. Before long, they acquire a confidence and a trust to come before the staff to share their more inner feelings and their more disturbing issues. By carefully and prudently observing them at first, staff can usually tell within a few weeks where *they are coming from and where they are at* with their program.

For various reasons, it is sometimes necessary to confront residents directly in the "home group" when there are issues relating to the integrity of the group as a whole or to destructive interpersonal dynamics. Residents are usually confronted if the negative aspects of their disease is an attempt to sabotage or damage the group process. In some instances, staff have to be more forceful with those who intimidate or undermine authority in front of the other residents. The residents are informed accordingly of certain behaviours which are simply not tolerated. Group leaders, by listening to them and by talking to them, can tell fairly well if the residents are *"only scratching the surface"* or if they are simply duping themselves and others. For example, if a new resident is sitting in the home group and trying to tell a staff member that he or she was a nice parent and a good spouse, when the staff knows full well from the person's history that the opposite is true, the staff will challenge the resident's dishonesty.

Confrontation of Resident to Resident: Peer Confrontation

Confrontation is initiated by one resident sharing with the other resident what she *has not* understood in the past about her various predicaments and what she now *does not* understand in the present. Previously, the alcoholic's big cry was *"no one understands me."* But when residents have that good feeling of being understood for the first time, they experience a powerful movement within themselves to reveal more.

Should a resident come to staff with a problem having to do with another member on program, the staff will encourage the resident to have a one-on-one with the resident involved and try to work it out that way first. Resident-to-resident confrontation is an ongoing process which is carried out in the context of the group meetings or under careful supervision. It also occurs after the various meetings and in the evenings.

Sometimes, the encounters will be conducted spontaneously and at other times with direction. In the one-on-ones, the *older residents* will encourage the newcomers to be honest about themselves. Residents might come to a group leader, who in turn, will recommend that they have a one-on-one with another resident who has experienced a similar type of problem but who has dealt with it constructively or who has effectively resolved it. So, confrontation generally takes place with a person confiding something with another person on program. Rather than giving direction, the one in whom the confiding has taken place can say, "I think you need to see staff on this matter." The live-in experience within the "therapeutic community" at Brentwood provides a rich beginning and culminates in graduation. What the residents learn on program are the tools of recovery and of living which they will be required to retain throughout their life-time.

CHAPTER 3

Brentwood's Philosophy[1]

Brentwood was originally located at 3020 Sandwich St. and opened its doors for treatment on Labor Day, 1974. It was here that Fr. Paul learned and gradually developed his unique approach. Never having a note before him in his presentations, he clearly used his keen mind and remarkable memory for facts and details coupled with a persevering faith in his vision. In his words:

⁂ The program unfolded simply by my being there and seeing what was needed. If the idea has any kernel of truth to it, if one perseveres and if one refuses to compromise or sell oneself short and not play games with it or "water it down", then the person will gradually know step-by-step how to apply it and will realize what direction to take in order to make it work. It flows as a natural progression. Alcoholism, basically, is not a substance abuse problem, but more importantly, it is a disease which fundamentally prevents people from being more fully human. ⁂

The Role of Three Key People
Undoubtedly, the three key people in the development of Brentwood have been Fr. Paul, the administrator and director along with Jim and Kay Ryan. Both Jim and Kay did all the counselling, attending to the funding and all the details necessary to ensure that the program ran effectively. Fr. Paul has always held both Jim and Kay in highest esteem for their dauntless and tenacious dedication. According to Fr. Paul: "Without their unwavering commitment Brentwood or Charity House would never have gotten off the ground."

For many years Jim and Kay Ryan worked untiringly twelve to fifteen hours per day without pay, using the money from the sale of their home to survive. As Fr. Paul so strongly demonstrates: "I could never have started either program without their motivation, effort,

---

1.   The following two chapters reflect the collective consciousness of the staff and their perception of the "Brentwood experience".

integrity, and perseverance, since they have poured their very heart and
soul into this recovery process."

Fr. Paul's own role at Brentwood is clear and succinct. In his
own words:

> ✳   Unquestionably as the leader it is necessary to be able to
> pull things together, to set an example, to give the spirit of courage
> or confidence and probably the fact of being able to make good
> sound decisions on the spot no matter what they are. My day cen-
> tres around the people who are the heart of Brentwood.   ✳

Kay Ryan sees her own role as "fitting in" to the whole scheme
of things and explains:

> ✳   Just being part of it and doing what I am told is rewarding
> for me. Since I was the only woman for the longest time, I was
> seen as a mother figure here to most of the men who came in before
> the women got involved. The men could come and talk to me about
> their wives or their children. What made me suited for this was
> the fact that I lived with an alcoholic husband myself and I knew
> the hurt and pain that this entailed. I was able to put myself in
> that wife's place instinctively. I knew, for instance, that if the man
> sent her roses that he would be "wearing them". She would throw
> them back at him because she would still be in her anger and
> resentment at the damage he caused the whole family.   ✳

The Key Ingredients of Brentwood

A key ingredient is Fr. Paul's charismatic nature, his talks and
how he instills into the fellowship *the spirit of caring, sharing* and *acceptance*. These include the staff and alumni, who are living the spirit
of Brentwood in their everyday lives. In his words:

> ✳   The people themselves will always say: "There's love here.
> We belong to a group that really understands and cares for us."
> Brentwood is very appropriate to the extent that whenever there
> is a need, there is always someone there to fill that specific need
> because of the number of people around.   ✳

A Dynamic Form of Intervention

Brentwood fosters an individual's growth process in a non-
threatening "family-type" setting. The care and the acceptance of one
alcoholic with the other alcoholic is what renders Brentwood such a
powerful experience. According to Fr. Paul:

> ✳   What makes Brentwood so *dynamic*, perhaps, though I use
> that adjective with some trepidation, are the alumni, those who
> after they have been through the program, still feel a need to re-

turn for themselves or a need to be there for the other alcoholic. I believe this is the key. In the beginning, they come back because of a fundamental need for it. The ninety days are not in themselves sufficient to make the lasting changes that are really necessary for the full growth to occur. So this need is an essential ingredient. Gradually, and only after a period of time when this need is being fulfilled, they begin to come back *in gratitude*. It is a natural progression. ✻

The Brentwood form of intervention is bold and daring because it confronts the heart and core of the resistant issues of each resident. It attacks the self-will which has run riot in the alcoholic. Brentwood feels that this basic perception got lost somehow and the distorted belief became more pronounced that as long as the alcoholic stops drinking then everything should be alright. As one alumnus remarks: "Personally, I stopped drinking and everything still wasn't right with me. I measure sobriety and recovery by the quality of a person's life."

Basic Assumptions Underlying the Brentwood Philosophy

Human spirituality is the underlying assumption of the Brentwood philosophy and alcoholics need to learn basic fundamental *spiritual principles*. It is a dynamic force which penetrates the heart of the issue of alcoholism. God has commanded: "You shall love the Lord your God with your whole heart, with your whole soul and with all your mind [and] you shall love your neighbor as yourself " (Matthew 22, p. 37). Brentwood maintains that every person is a child of God and has within her the capacity through responsible action to choose a better way of life. Each person has a latent goodness which needs to be activated. Fr. Paul explains:

> ✻ The primary assumption at Brentwood is the basic need which people have to be happy. Brentwood can help them accomplish this basic need because it has found a successful way to assist people to become happier in their lives. ✻

Brentwood's Spiritual Model of Recovery

Most people are caught up in a false sense of *religiosity*. They can spew off about religion but are unable to internalize it and express it effectively in everyday practice. It is believed that very few churchgoers have been able to make religion a truly *inner experience*. Some can go through the motions by rote but have not developed the art of how to internalize and how to operationalize their beliefs. Thus, their religion remains barren, detached, fragmented and cerebral: a phoney exercise in self-will. Brentwood teaches the essence and meaning of life on a daily basis.

The Brentwood spirit helps alcoholics to relate as human beings and it shows them how they need one another. No resident can "go it alone". They are called upon to ponder: *"How do they fit into society? How do they perform more effectively on their job? How do they become a better parent, a better spouse and a better son or daughter?"* Brentwood keeps returning to the whole concept of family and the sense of community which is spiritually rooted. They can now live with the possibility of *making legitimate mistakes* but they can also *forgive themselves* and they can forgive others. According to Kay Ryan:

> ✳   The model is really difficult to describe in a few simple words. Many people are looking at alcoholism differently because of Brentwood. Some facilities are now using it as a model of recovery in their own areas. It has to be experienced in order to appreciate its true worth and value. It is difficult to put something which is spiritual into a written language that others can fully understand unless they are fully engrossed in it.   ✳

The Uniqueness of Brentwood's Approach to Alcoholism

The spiritual model on which the program is built as well as the specific manner in which the various elements of sharing, confiding and consulting are expressed and interwoven make it unique. Residents are able to internalize a new way of thinking, feeling and doing and as a result can be more honest, loving and responsible in their actions. According to Fr. Paul:

> ✳   Brentwood's unique approach stems from the basic concept that everyone is a human being and alcoholism itself has very little to do with the so-called disease of the booze and the drugs. Our emphasis with this whole issue of alcoholism is on the need to be a human being and the ability to live our lives in and through other people. The alcoholic has gone astray from peace and happiness and Brentwood provides the tools by which the individual can come *back on track*. It entails people being human and not being afraid to let other people be human with them.   ✳

Brentwood has always provided a service for people whenever the need has arisen and has made every attempt *not* to turn anyone away. It believes that everyone who comes to its door should have an equal chance to turn their lives around and its basic policy is *not to give up on anyone* who can benefit from its program. Kay Ryan vividly recalls a critical incident which occurred in this respect:

> ✳   There's an example when we were on Sandwich street where we had a very young eighteen-year-old whom we had in residence on three different occasions. Each time he would go back out and

mess his life up again by either getting drunk, getting in trouble or ending up in jail. He was back again. In those days we only had a small staff. So when we had a problem like this young lad, Fr. Paul would get us together in a meeting to decide if we would admit this person or not. So when I was told that this individual was coming back I originally said: "I'm sorry but I am not voting for his return because of his poor track record. There is just no way."

In the meantime, just before the meeting, there was a letter on my desk which contained this teenager's inventory and which really opened my eyes in terms of the pain and hardship which he had endured. I thought to myself: "Any wonder this poor youth has failed every time." Consequently, I went into the meeting and I voiced the necessity of *taking him back*. And Fr. Paul in amazement quipped: "You want to take him back? Just a few minutes ago you were vehemently opposed to his return." I said: "Something has happened since. I read a letter he wrote to Jim and I can now understand why he is the way he is and where he is coming from. He is so full of hate and simply despises everybody. But he seems to have taken a liking to Jim and appears able to relate to him." He was admitted again and was able to remain sober for years after that. This brings me back to the point of not making any hasty judgements on anyone. Even in my own experience, I have had to look back and reflect and reconsider the evidence and act accordingly. ✻

Determining the Length of Time on Program

The effective quality of the Brentwood program is in some ways attributed to the length of time required of most residents. The 90-day program has always been the mainstay of Brentwood and continues to be the most useful one if people are to have a successful attempt at getting a handle on this disease. There are fewer and fewer 60-day programs now. As Fr. Paul explains:

✻   We continue to believe that everybody still needs the ninety days. This is our basic program and it is unlikely that we will ever change that stance since it is so fundamental. One has to take into consideration the whole context of the person who comes to Brentwood for admission. The determination is made by us and normally speaking we will listen to a person who is self-employed and who is unable to come on program for more than twenty-eight days. There has to be reasonable circumstances to grant the limited twenty-eight days, not simply because the person has asked for it or the fact that it is all the individual wants. It has to be determined on a more honest and responsible basis because if twenty-eight days is all that the person wants, there is likely not enough willingness or sincerity to go any further than that.

Those who are self-employed are given primary consideration
because of the financial pressures or the fact that they will not
have any income for two or three months. Another consideration
is sickness, family or repeaters who are usually considered for
twenty-eight days. This is the program favored at this time by the
government. Children in school are considered for twenty-eight
days so that their school year is not jeopardized. The decisions
made are based on practical reasons.   ✳

The Ninety-Day Program
The ninety-day program which is more or less the standard, is
an in-residence program (Duncan, 1989). Each resident is in domicile
for at least ten weeks after which he or she usually commutes as a
preparatory link to discharge. Each resident is obliged to follow very
stringent rules and regulations as part of the discipline which is required
for effective recovery. The resident has to ask permission for weekend
passes and passes during the day to attend to various personal or business requirements. Permission to leave property is usually given by the
group leader. Granting such permission is based upon the leader's awareness of the resident's motivation on program, the living conditions at
home and the ability of the resident to be trusted in terms of abstinence
while off property.

Through Fr. Paul's talks, the one-on-ones, the guidance and support of the group leaders, and the home group meetings, the residents
become acquainted with Brentwood's approach to the disease of alcoholism. After graduation, there is a follow-up which includes attendance at
two to three meetings per week.

The Sixty-Day Program
The sixty-day program, established in 1988, is for people who
fall between the other two categories of programs. It is for those who
need more than the 28-day program and particularly for those who cannot attend the 90 days. It might be for sickness in the family or for
some honest and legitimate reason that would not allow the 90 days. It
may also be for those who live considerably far away from the local
area. Those who graduate from the 60-day program are asked to attend
the Brentwood meetings which are accessible in their own area. If these
are not available, they are encouraged to go to AA. These graduates are
also invited to make phone contact, where possible, with Brentwood
alumni in neighboring areas. The 60-day program is modelled on the
90-day program and has much of the same components as the 90-day
program.

The Twenty-Eight-Day Program
The 28-day program which is supported financially and overseen
by the Provincial Ministry of Health, has been in progress since 1988.

The Ministry provides financial backing for a total of thirty beds and also makes provisions for after-care and for day treatment.

The length of stay depends on the varying needs of people. The 28 days is usually for those who are self-employed and, who for financial reasons, cannot come on program for a longer period. It often depends on the time they have available from work or family situations. The decision is made based upon the specific requirements of each individual. It is also for repeaters or former graduates or alumni who return for a "tune-up". The 28 days is also for people of Essex County who are restricted in available time due to school, their sick-benefit plan and the fact that they might be self-employed and cannot afford the time off. Some employers and industry administration allow only 28 days.

Residents who do the 28-day program are required to carry through on a four-month follow-up before graduating. They must attend at least four meetings per week, either in the morning or the afternoon, to accommodate those who are on shift work. Their attendance is carefully monitored and they are asked to leave if they do not successfully complete this out-of-residence requirement.

Brentwood's Effectiveness

Fr. Paul identifies the element of effectiveness in this way:

*   My whole initial experience with the alcoholic and with alcoholism within AA revolved around the love, the care and the understanding of the alcoholic. This was the key. I have had enough experience with AA to know that my approach works. *

Brentwood functions effectively in proportion to the people's willingness to make it work, those who are willing to change their lives from *what they have been to what they need to be*. Brentwood offers a strong *guarantee* that the program will work as long as there is a willingness to be honest and to follow direction. The effectiveness of the program is dependent upon the *willingness of the person to surrender*, if only in a very limited way at first. Residents have to trust that people in charge of the program know something about this disease that they do not know. As one staff member comments:

*   I have seen people who are not able to handle this surrender and thus leave the program. I have seen others who have actually turned their lives around. Brentwood has had a very profound effect on the very core of a person's mind and heart. I consider myself to have been one of those persons. *

According to Fr. Paul:

*   In terms of our effectiveness, "the proof is in the pudding" as the facts speak for themselves. Brentwood is effective not only because we believe in it but also because we know the results. The people "grab" it whether we are at the schools, the prisons or regardless of whether they are alcoholic themselves in the traditional sense in which society sees alcoholism. They know once they are shown that it is the truth. They know that this is what is missing in their lives. This is what they have been looking for and what has eluded them for so long.

Some are simply not ready to respond to the truth. They do not have the willingness to grow up and live life responsibly, to take the steps or make the necessary sacrifice to turn it around and to live a life like this because of their inability to really trust. They have had the problem since they were very young. They have had the fear of it and they have had to devise a way of living without it while pretending that either they had it, that it was not that important or that it was impossible to achieve. For some, even at twenty-five or forty, it is so ingrained that they walk away from it because they cannot handle it.   ✳

Brentwood claims a 70–75% success rate in terms of the individuals who come through its program, as well as their spouses, the children, the aunts, the uncles, the grandmothers, the grandfathers, or friends and acquaintances. Another staff member adds:

✳   Brentwood would certainly hold its own if compared to other facilities in terms of both its "success rate" and its "credibility". It can prove its effectiveness in terms of the quality of people's lives after they have completed the actual program and as they continue to practice their recovery. If we are talking about the physical sobriety (no booze or drugs), Brentwood accomplishes this very well. But if, in addition, we are talking about reneging self-will, living more fulfilling lives and about our increased involvement in the community, then we are addressing the major aspect of Brentwood's success.

In terms of our illness, we have the confirmation of how well we are doing, how well our sobriety is going through the other recovering alcoholic. We are reminded every day by the fellowship of whether or not we are in self-pity or wallowing in the "poor me's" which, in effect, is our *predisposition* to self-indulgence. If left to our own devices, we might misinterpret our own recovery, think we are doing well, when in reality we might be "missing it". It is not up to me alone to determine how well things are going. The Brentwood community keeps us honest. Brentwood is well-recognized as effective in the community in political circles and in religious circles. Brentwood has been at a peak in terms of admissions from diverse places. If we are not doing a good job, why are so many seeking admission? If Brentwood were not doing a good job, why would so many want to come back and continue to grow? People get better as a result of its treatment approach. It is not just the individual looking at his or her own sobriety, it is the witness of the recovered people in the community, how well they are functioning and how well they are perceived by others as living life effectively that makes an impact.   ✳

Brentwood: A Cost-Effective Facility

No individual who comes to Brentwood is ever denied help because of lack of money. Brentwood has always had a saying which in great measure was based on faith: "If we take care of each resident, the rest will take care of itself." Because of its spiritually-based ideology, *"helping those who cannot pay,"* it refuses to charge some of the exorbitant costs of other programs and teaches that something which is spiritually fulfilling is not given a material *"price tag"*. It has no set fee but merely asks the residents to be honest about their program and about the amount they can contribute financially. Brentwood relies to a large extent on outside contributions and it looks to alumni for raising funds.

Brentwood touches so many lives through the integral role of the alumni who are continually helping those who are on program. As Fr. Paul illustrates:

> ✳   The most cost-effective element in Brentwood is the fact that we emphasize, and are fortunate to have, numerous alumni in the course of any one day. Our primary philosophy hinges on the alumni who return faithfully on a daily basis. It is not necessarily the staff, as important as they are, who are the main source of recovery for the people who come to us. The alumni are an essential and necessary element. Brentwood would not work if it relied solely on staff. The alumni are the backbone.   ✳

One can readily appreciate cost-effectiveness when one looks at the total number of people on program: two-hundred at any given time which means 71,200 client days annually and with a budget of $2,000,000, to a little over $28.00 per day. It is a marvel that so much can be done for so many by so few for so little. Brentwood's expenditure is about a tenth of what it would cost in a comparable facility. One staff member, for example, who went to a 28-day program which cost almost $10,000.00, laments: "I only learned about the mechanics of drug use"!

The Impact of the "Home Group"

Due to Brentwood's continued expansion, it has been necessary to provide a "home group". According to Fr. Paul:

> ✳   Because of the increasing number of residents on program, positive measures have had to be taken to allow the Brentwood experience to be more personal. This provides a lot more order and permits things to be done in a more effective and responsible way.

The smaller "home groups" afford more structure and make it a lot easier for staff to be able to monitor where people are in their programs. There is a staff leader for every twenty-five to thirty people, one who is both responsible and capable of ensuring that each resident is being accountable day by day. Through the groups, the leaders can tell if each member of the group is going about the program in an honest and responsible way in terms of the sincerity of her self-disclosure to the others. It ensures that the alcoholic will get honest with the others on program.   ✳

Persons upon admittance to program are assigned to one of nine groups. They are in the same home group from the day they come on program to the time they leave. Three of these groups are for women, seven for men. Each group has a staff leader who is a former graduate. The home group deals with inventory, sharing and confiding on the theme of the day, and with an honesty session on how each person is doing and dealing with her program.
All the residents are asked to explain how they think they are doing in their program. They are requested to identify what is *going well* and what is *not going well* in their lives. Then the group leader may ask someone else in the group to comment on the person's self-disclosure, if it is seen as honest or not, whether the other group members think the person may be simply "conning" or if the person is failing to get sincere about her recovery process. This is a form of *caring confrontation* in the group and it provides feedback to the group member as to whether or not she is "watering down" her program. The other group members who are with each other day in and day out know where the person is coming from, and whether she is being deceitful or not. They act as a "reality buffer" to verify that the resident is being authentic. If residents cannot test reality here and if they cannot give the honest feedback, they are less likely to be able to test it on the outside with family, the workplace or the community.
Developing the ability to trust happens in the home group, and the degree of sharing is enhanced as time unfolds. It is in the continual reassurance of warmth, security and belonging that they can say:

✳   Wow, I feel I can divulge anything to these people. If another resident can share an incident which is so damaging and perverse and if they can be so genuinely accepted by the group, I don't have to be afraid to self-disclose because I know I will not be rejected for anything that I share no matter how serious or perverse it may have been. I have the confidence that the group will accept me just as they have accepted the others. There is a powerful process which occurs in the "home group" which is a decisive aspect of the ongoing treatment of each resident on program.   ✳

Group leaders realize how important it is to insure that everyone gets an opportunity to share. Sometimes they break the group up into smaller sections so that all the residents get the opportunity to share and not feel left out. The leaders also encourage group members to provide feedback to one another so that after someone has shared, each member has an occasion to communicate to the person who did the sharing.

The group is an arena where residents can be deeply invested in each other's growth. As they get to know each other so intricately, they cultivate an ardent bond. They identify with each other as a "unified family". It has been the Brentwood experience that those residents who indeed stay sober and have a healthy recovery are the ones who form friendships, bond within the home group, and maintain that bond. They call each other by phone when they leave and they make a commitment to come back to meetings after they graduate. Not only have they made a number of close friends but they have widened their circle of meaningful relationships, something that up to now has been foreign to them. This same caring and sharing process is continued with their own families and is extended in the community in which they are involved.

The group process is always evolving. The residents are at different stages of recovery: some are new to the program, others are in a certain number of weeks and some are ready to graduate. This variety provides a very rich input for all the residents. The older residents tend to be an inspiration to the new people on program because they are not just "talking" the program but they are "walking" the program. The new residents, in turn, are a powerful reminder to the older ones of where they were when they first came on program.

The Importance of Being a Group Leader

Staff consider themselves very fortunate to be group leaders because they feel it fortifies and heightens the quality of their own lives. They are able to share their own experiences each day with the residents. Even though people leave the program at various junctures, the leaders always have new residents with whom to share. They never forget the once painful journey they travelled themselves, knowing that it is important for them not only to remember their past roots but also to realize in the process that they are being helped because their investment is coming back to them a hundredfold. One staff member, touched by the role of group leader states:

✻   Each morning as I make my own commitments, I have a deep sense of gratitude for the respect that I am given at Brentwood. I try as hard as I can just to be "one with" each resident because it is such an important role. It is not simply the knowledge that I have gained over the years which is important but the fact that I am able to lead them from a world of deception, of ridicule or from a world of being "put down" to a sphere of honor and integrity where they can build themselves up as well as help others. This way of life, this searching for and living the truth in our lives is God-inspired and God-given. How I govern myself at Brentwood impacts on each resident who imitates my example. Additionally, how I conduct myself in the community is important because I represent Brentwood and the recovering alcoholic.   *

The Role of the Group Leader

The role of the group leader is simply "to be there" for residents, to care for them and to act as a safeguard in ensuring that the residents are doing their program, and to provide the leadership. The group leader also keeps the meetings going smoothly and deals with any problems that may arise. If there are any real issues that they cannot deal with, they bring these to the attention of one of the counselling staff.

The leaders also intervene when they notice something that needs to be confronted or clarified in a person . The leaders also deal with persons on a one-to-one basis as required. They comment on the various written inventories. They might routinely assist members in the home group or outside of the group, give week-end and daily permissions or contact spouses or parents of members in the group.

The group leaders have to assert themselves to the extent necessary for the smooth operation of the group. They are called to initiate, encourage and motivate residents not only by mere words but more so by example. They not only talk "to" the residents but also share "with" them, sensitive to the fact that they are "alcoholic".

The staff are not caught up in the power but are grateful to be able to provide a service to others. The role of the group leaders is best captured in the saying: "If you walk in front of me, I may not be able to follow. If you walk behind me, I may not be able to lead. Just walk beside me and be my friend." Most alcoholics have attempted inappropriately to be the centre of attention all their lives. This is quite a switch from the way they acted in the past. They wanted to "do their own thing" without restraints. Being a group leader, with the humility that comes with it, is a real role reversal for most leaders.

The Role of the Group Members

Members are placed in small groups not merely to actively listen, but they are called on to contribute verbally and to feel a sense of belonging. Although this is the one thing the alcoholic was never able to do, it becomes possible through the *caring and sharing*, for this reason. The residents are both encouraged and at times challenged to contribute verbally.

It is the responsibility of residents to attend all group meetings, to pay attention to the group leader, to have respect for the leader, to have respect for one another and to be upright about their own life and process of recovery.

The role of group members is to share their experiences and to offer each other the hope that recovery can work. They realize that they are not *special*, in the negative sense of the term, but that they all suffer from the same disease and the same defects of character: no matter where they come from they all have the same problem. It is important that the group members themselves be able to act for the good of the group, to challenge individuals in the "honesty meetings" and to be there for the group as a whole as well as for each individual.

The "home group" could not survive unless they relied upon one another. Each individual depends on the other person for her sobriety. There is no isolation possible when each member is open to share and to receive the insights of the group members. The one-on-ones are heightened by means of the small home group where so much of the program's richness comes together.

Can Brentwood Stand on Its Own Without the Person of Fr. Paul?

A question which arises quite frequently is the fear of Brentwood possibly falling apart once Fr. Paul leaves the helm. Some have misgivings that it will be almost impossible to replace a man who virtually has done the work of five or six people, since he is seen as a "difficult act to follow."

There is no doubt that a Brentwood without the person of Fr. Paul will have its struggles, the growing pains of forging an extension of what he initiated some twenty-five years ago. It has been a breakthrough for him to loosen the reins and to pass them on to others. It is clearly a challenge which will draw staff and alumni to a richer dimension. Fr. Paul is making a concerted effort to assure that the spirit of Brentwood grows and prospers. This "letting-go" pattern is being seen more and more as Fr. Paul gradually prepares for retirement. He is carrying out his plan in reality by his careful delegation and transfer of roles to a well-trained staff and by curtailing his workload.

Fr. Paul has very carefully prepared for his ultimate departure by having transmitted to the staff and the fellowship the necessary tools to continue the mission which he diligently began. As those in the fellowship work the program, they garner a strength and a confidence to continue the Brentwood spirit and to uphold its challenge. Just as they have received the "gift of sobriety" in their lives, they want to extend and advance this gift to those who are still struggling with the disease. Fr. Paul is the foundation but the building process is people, fellowship and alumni.

The lessons that were started originally with Fr. Paul were intended to enter the hearts of the fellowship so as to transform their lives each day into effective actions. One ardent staff member consoles himself with this thought:

✳   I see Fr. Paul as the messenger and we as alumni who have become the message. Brentwood conveys a fairly strong moral incentive to the community—*if you do what these alumni have done, you too can change your life.* Fr. Paul, at the daily meetings, claims that the messengers sit in the alumni side of the meeting hall and he exclaims: "You alumni with each other are the true message, not only to one other, but also to the community when they witness people like yourselves who have changed your lives for the better." Inasmuch as Fr. Paul originated the message, we now have the heart of the message and currently we can go out and proclaim it. It is within the splendor of this context that Brentwood is not solely dependent upon Fr. Paul.   ✳

What is important to Fr. Paul is the integrity of the program and the assurance and confirmation that it will be passed on. Considering the spirit that he has promulgated among the fellowship, there is every reason to believe that Brentwood will survive. Fr. Paul has always emphasized his confidence in the alumni and is optimistic that Brentwood can exist without him. The staff in turn are confident that the spirit of Brentwood will live in the alumni and those people whom Fr. Paul will designate when the time eventually comes for his departure from the helm. Members of the staff are conscious of his total investment and accomplishments.

Judging by every indicator, Brentwood will, therefore, continue to survive. The substance of the lectures will likely remain the same and the spirit of both Brentwood and the alumni will prevail.

Brentwood: A Public Trust

In the beginning, Brentwood, for various reasons, was not accepted favorably by the local community. Fr. Paul views this initial resistance positively in terms of his understanding of human nature:

> ✳   I think this is normal since anything that is new in terms of dealing with people, this type of "watchdog" role, provides a distinctive safeguard for the community. We have made a great deal of progress in terms of having a positive influence upon the community but there will always be doubters and back-biters as is common in any locality. I am not shocked by this in the least and I rather welcome the safeguards as a means of accountability from the community. Otherwise, we are being naive to expect even the majority to like us, to agree with us or to be interested in what we are doing.   ✳

When Father Paul first started Charity House, it was difficult to get things off the ground and deal with some of the opposition. In fact, some people were opposed to it for quite a while. They were very much afraid of the word alcoholic and they perceived alcoholics as a "bunch of drunks" stumbling with brown paper bags covering their bottle. The people in the surrounding area were afraid for themselves. Convincing the community was a slow process. Brentwood had to prove itself by helping to overcome this stigma in the wider community. Brentwood has demonstrably gained this trust and confidence the hard way—by working with the "hard core" alcoholics. Kay Ryan mentions:

* It was difficult in the beginning, since we were working with the down-and-out alcoholic, those who had reached their bottom, with nowhere to live, no one to care about them, their only friend being the bottle and their biggest worry, where would they get the money for their next drink. The purchase of the I.O.O.F. building was not without its problems. When the news got out that the I.O.O.F. hall was going to be used to feed, clothe, and house the down-and-out people in the area, a petition was taken up by residents and businessmen in the area to prevent Charity House from opening. Undaunted by this new development, Fr. Paul forged ahead. The locals soon found that their fears were unfounded, and ironically a number of residents and their children ended up helping us serve meals once we opened. (Brentwood, p. 8, 1989) *

Over the years, Brentwood has grown from infancy to adulthood by a faithful allegiance to its own principles and to its founder. Brentwood gained the respect and the trust of the community and, in turn, the community is now accepting Brentwood. And realizing how effective it is as an organization. Brentwood has achieved a very favorable acclaim from the Provincial Government which has been amply shown in the financial support which the government has provided and which it continues to provide.

Brentwood: On Longterm Sobriety and Recovery

The Brentwood program is successful to the extent that a person is prepared to make a substantial investment in the process of recovery, does what he or she is told, persists in the sharing and confiding, and uses the tools that are provided. The fellowship is a living testimony of the success of Brentwood. Positive things are heard in the community, at work and in the various churches, of how a spouse, a son, a daughter, a sister, a brother, a relative or a friend was helped through Brentwood. There are some alumni who date back to the very beginning of Brentwood when it was referred to as Charity House and who have maintained their sobriety. The testimony is in the thousands of alumni who are working this way of life. One staff member says:

* For me it has been twelve years since I came to Brentwood. I try to be a living example. It has worked for me. My family tells me they are pleased with my program. The important part is the positive effect it has upon me and the important people in my life. *

The Non-Alcoholic Question

It has often been questioned by people who have been associated in one way or another with Brentwood: "Does Brentwood treat people who are not 'alcoholic'"? To answer this question effectively, a great deal depends on one's definition of the "alcoholic", of "alcoholism" and of "addiction". To this query, Fr. Paul responds: "According to society's definition of 'alcoholic', yes! But not according to our definition." One staff member explains:

＊   If we are talking about what we believe is the personality of the alcoholic, we do not treat anyone who is not alcoholic. In terms of the more formal, clinical definition, they are, more than likely, not alcoholic. If one is looking at the broader and more comprehensive sense of the compulsions and impulses in the alcoholic, the self-centeredness and so on, then, there has not been a person who has gone through Brentwood who did not belong here nor one who could not be helped by the richness of this program.   ＊

Brentwood's program works for any person, even the non-alcoholic who is trying to grow. According to Kay Ryan: "Brentwood works for everyone. For instance, I do not consider myself an alcoholic and it *certainly has worked for me*. In fact, the beauty of Brentwood is that it can be used by all human beings." According to Fr. Paul:

＊   Practically anyone and everyone would benefit from our program. The only people who would not benefit from it are those who are not ready or willing. Yet, in a sense, this is not true because of our conviction that the people who do not stay in Brentwood still leave with some kind of an impact having been made on them, even those who are only here for a few days. These people benefit from it because it makes them sensitive to and aware of what the problem really is and they will not *think* the same or *feel* the same about themselves after Brentwood even if they have only stayed a day or so. Neither will they find it as easy to kid themselves in terms of *acting* out their disease or in realizing what the real issue is to their problem whether or not there is any help for them at the moment. Basically, the alcoholic has failed in his or her response to nature in terms of his or her *thinking, feeling and doing*.   ＊

Brentwood's Candidates

Though people with serious mental problems are sometimes not helped, there have been numerous cases where Brentwood has been successful with them. Brentwood is not afraid to deal with people who are severely handicapped, whether physically, mentally, emotionally or psychologically, and who seek help. However, people who have difficulty with the spiritual concept of surrender or cooperation and who feel that recovery can be done in one's own way, time and place, would have much greater difficulty in adapting to the Brentwood philosophy and in benefiting from what it has to offer.

People who are closed and are unable to make the commitment required for the rigor and discipline which the Brentwood recovery program demands would have difficulty. A person who is sixty to sixty-five and set in his or her ways, or a person who is sixteen or seventeen years old but does not have the necessary motivation to make a lasting commitment would experience considerable difficulty. Also, those who are controlled by a false intellectual pride would most likely have great difficulty in making the necessary transition since they would refuse to submit to anyone else's authority.

Furthermore, a person who is defiant and simply does not want help may be unable to adjust to the program. Likewise, the same might be true for a person who has no motivation or is not prepared to make a commitment and a rebellious person who does not want to change and who does not want to grow might present a problem.

Almost anybody can grasp Brentwood's philosophy because its principles are so simple. As one staff member muses:

⁂ If you can explain why a person can come into Brentwood who is unable to even speak English and nonetheless, leave with something spiritual, then something has to be said for the power and depth of its approach. I have been blessed with two or three residents with similar circumstances who left here feeling great and yet they could not speak English. They could communicate by looks, expressions and feelings. In one case we had to get a translator to help out. In another incident, a former resident is back with his wife and family and doing exceptionally well. ⁂

CHAPTER 4

The Brentwood Program

In this section we will deal with questions about the Brentwood program that are frequently asked, such as the large size of the group in therapy, the role of the group leaders, the procedures for recovery and treating residents, the problem of recidivism and the sources of referrals. We will also look at other aspects, such as the treatment of women alcoholics at Brentwood and the involvement of families of alcoholics.

Program and Group Size

Brentwood believes that because it is a spiritual program the more people it has, the more successful the program can be. While residents are at Brentwood, they have a distinct opportunity to work on getting along with other people, accepting people and redirecting their lives with other people in mind. Fr. Paul's views are quite clear on this point:

> ✳   We face the element of quantity on a daily basis. We don't buy the theory that the larger we get, the weaker we become, that we are not going to be able to carry out our work. If we were strictly a business organization or if we were just looking at it from a standpoint of trying to help people get off drugs or the booze, that might be true, but when one is talking about improving people's lives and their becoming better human beings for the rest of their lives, then the more people we have the more success we have. Consequently, the more people that are here for one another the more the whole program just blossoms.
>
> Probably only the people who have been through it can completely understand the full implications. It is difficult to tell people about the program unless they have experienced it. Take, for example, the area of forgiveness. This issue is so serious that the alcoholic might have to experience forgiveness five hundred to a thousand times before it kicks in. So forgiveness is not just another word. Forgiveness has to be experienced over and over again in a face to face encounter with another human being where they

experience acceptance, trust, respect and the sense of being reconciled. They have to experience it in order for them to believe it, to trust it and to accept it before it is going to have an impact on them. The alcoholic has layers of this "baloney," this resentment, this hardness that has to be peeled and peeled like one might peel an orange or onion skin, one layer at a time. This type of forgiveness or unraveling cannot be compared to a stereotyped religion, as far as we are concerned here at Brentwood, where you *ask for forgiveness*, where you *are forgiven* and where you genuinely *feel forgiven*. Others have tried and with very little success.

It is in experiencing the love, the warmth and the forgiveness over and over again, that the alcoholic feels whole and renewed. If we only have ten or twelve people this would not be sufficient, it would just scratch the surface. But if we have two or three hundred, the alcoholic then has sufficient opportunity. On the other side of the coin, the residents have more opportunities to experience their reactions to countless people they don't like, people whom they have never associated with before. Now they are forced to eat with them, live with them and listen to them. They have to then make an effort to welcome these encounters as opportunities to overcome hates, resentments and angers. They just can't walk away from the others or just have abrupt confrontations with them as they have so deceptively done in the past. They now are presented with opportunities to work the program responsibly. Not only do they receive the forgiveness from one another, as well as the trust and the love that they need but they also have these tremendous occasions every day to work on their own defects. The more people we have, the more chances we have. The fewer people we have the fewer opportunities are available. The spiritual is developed with the people they deal with in all walks of life and with people of all ages. If one doesn't understand the spiritual and how it works, then one can be confused and discouraged by numbers.

For the first time, our residents receive the love of others as real. For this to occur, they have to humble themselves and recognize that they are not *superior* or "*special*". They can no longer distance or isolate themselves from others but have to become "*part of*". If there were only a few individuals, there would not be sufficient opportunities for everybody. We had the experience when we were small in numbers that our program was lacking in this respect. Now we have the experience and the numbers. The more in number, the deeper and the more responsible is our program. We increase and multiply. It is the opposite of what society really believes is effective.

Alcoholics have never disciplined themselves to listen to others. Having some twenty-nine people or so in a small group gives them an opportunity to listen to the pain of those who are sharing their story. Alcoholics have to learn to wait and they have to realize that the world does not respond immediately to their "beck and call." It is felt that the residents, before their admission to Brentwood, were so cut and dried about things, so clearly obstinate in their minds whether they liked the people next to them or not that they would walk away and have nothing to do with others.

The size of the group provides them with the chance to leave their own narrow world of preoccupation and to give themselves genuinely to someone else. Soon enough their turn will come to speak and to be heard in the group. It does not necessarily have to happen immediately.　✳

Group Leader Role at Brentwood

The job of staff members at Brentwood is first of all to live responsibly as a "recovering alcoholic," to provide a personal example for others to follow and to help those on program. The staff see their role here as carrying the message which was given to them by Fr. Paul and which they have internalized and now share with the residents, the alumni and the fellowship.

The group leaders can act as a referral for each resident. Also, when residents are leaving the program upon graduation, they ensure that they are going to have accommodations and they make sure that they will have a place to live. They make sure in the residents' tenth or eleventh week that they are honestly and sincerely on job search and actually out there looking for employment. Some staff members work with the residents along with various social service programs in the local community. They are all involved in the duty office as need be on a rotating basis and ensure that all of the jobs of each resident are taken care of. They attend to the smooth operation of the kitchen as far as the work of the residents is concerned.

Job descriptions include diverse areas of involvement. Staff members lead the groups, see that the residents do what they are supposed to do, give them support and guide them in the proper direction. They sometimes have to deal with some of the lawyers and the Children's Aid. They occasionally have public relations work to do. They are involved with the parents if it has to do with the younger ones on program.

One staff member is involved with the prisons, with the professional group, the police group, with the lawyers in the community and with the sex offenders' group. The role of the staff is to share with the residents and to direct the home groups and see that they stay on topic. Major reports are brought to Fr. Paul where necessary. Staff inform Fr. Paul as to what is going on in the group and about each individual in that group if need be. Some are responsible for allotting certain residents to work the bingo, dispensing the tobacco ration and taking responsibility in the duty office. They also answer in written form the submissions of each resident in their charge.

Staff Self-Disclosure:
Telling Their Own Story to Others

There is a transparency among the staff members in terms of their sharing their own story. Justification for such disclosure is provided by Fr. Paul as he explains his own approach:

> ✳ I'll use examples from my own life frequently if they apply. I just don't tell my story for any which reason or on whim. It has to be appropriate. I'll give examples from my life if I think it will be beneficial to people and if I am convinced that it actually fits their circumstances. ✳

Most staff members freely tell their story to those able to relate to, or benefit from it. As one female staff relates:

> ✳ If residents tell me something that clicks in with my experience, I tell them about something similar that happened to me through my husband's drinking. This way, you develop a sort of bond and connectedness with the person, where you feel good about it and where you realize that this could happen to me as well as to them. ✳

Staff relate candidly with the residents, particularly in the small groups, whenever the opportunity arises and another alcoholic needs to hear their story, or whenever the public will gain insight into the nature and seriousness of the disease. As one staff member remarks:

> ✳ I don't try preaching it to everyone but if I get a chance to share or to witness to a person I feel is having a problem, I simply speak about myself and I allow them to receive it as they see fit. Many times I get some of the most "spiritual shots" through people who are unaware that I am making an impact upon them. I believe that somewhere down the line what I share will "rub off". ✳

Residents' Initial Encounter at Brentwood

There are many reasons why people come to Brentwood. Some come for the wrong reasons, for example, to get their wives back or their children, to regain their jobs, to get the courts "off their back" and some —merely to "fill in time." Some are rebellious and angry because they have been forced into Brentwood by the courts. Others come genuinely seeking help. But whatever the motive, most come with profound anxiety, greatly in need of understanding and sensitive handling much as accident victims come to the emergency department of a hospital.

The very fear of rejection is not an uncommon factor among most new residents. Kay Ryan describes her experience with clients in their initial apprehension: "I would first give them a cup of coffee and sit them down and talk with them. This reduces their anxiety and makes them feel more comfortable. It helps to make them feel more relaxed because they are so scared." Some have heard different stories about Brentwood and they are apprehensive as to just what is going to happen to them. They are on very shaky and fragile ground. Others are even afraid to be angry. The scenarios vary depending upon what brought them to Brentwood. For the most part, their spirits are broken and their hearts are shattered. Some are petrified because they are making a *quantum leap* into the unknown which leaves them uncertain as to what they can expect. Some, in their fear, either scrutinize the people on program or feel that they want to run: they want to "get out of here." As they gain insight into the heart of the disease, however, they approach the realm of alcoholism and addiction very differently. Most residents, in fact, have harbored a host of unresolved emotions and pent-up feelings which become more pronounced upon their arrival at Brentwood.

Adjusting to Brentwood can be a very trying experience which is further hindered by a strong sense of inferiority. Others appear very arrogant, act with a sense of superiority and try to "take over." One young resident, for example, thought he was at Brentwood to "straighten others out." Another, a Karate expert and a professional caregiver, tried to baffle the staff and the fellowship with words. Some act as if they have no problems and assume an attitude of indifference. Some simply fail to listen or refuse to take direction. Some present an attitude of "knowing it all" and act as if they are completely helpless and "know absolutely nothing." Others play "down-right-scared" or they play "rough and tough" with a chip on their shoulder, saying to themselves with a totally negative attitude: "You're not going to move me. I don't have a problem." Some are fairly resistant and rather negative, having all their lives done "their own thing," but suddenly at Brentwood, they are confronted with rules which go against the grain.

When individuals decide to turn to Brentwood, it is understandable that they feel insecurity and mistrust, as they meet other people on program and encounter a whole new way of life. The initial entrance of the majority of residents somewhat resembles a child's first day at school—scared, nervous, disturbed and agitated. They ask themselves: "What have I done? What's going to happen to me? Is this, at long last, the place?" However, others, the minority, approach Brentwood with defiance and a seemingly arrogant exterior.

Fr. Paul is always sensitive to each new resident and, in his talks, manages to get at the underlying issues, triggering a conscious awareness in that new resident. Fr. Paul recognizes that alcoholics have had a *bad break in life*, that their way of life has been very painful and obscure, and most feel that they have been "shortchanged" by either their parents, their relatives or their friends. The majority feel sorry for themselves and lament: "I didn't get the breaks in life, I had the wrong 'this and the wrong that'...I didn't have the opportunities that others so generously had. I feel I was cheated." As Fr. Paul sees it:

✳   We are very fortunate in the way Brentwood is set up. Initially, each resident is assigned a person to be with them practically for the whole day simply to assist in helping break down some of the fears and to "be there" with each one of them. The overall spirit of the fellowship, where the vast majority are happy to be here and have a very positive spirit, makes those coming in for the first time feel a little more welcome and a little more positive because of the optimistic attitude and feeling which they sense in the whole of the fellowship. Everyone that they meet, staff and others, make it a little easier for them to feel good about their decision to come into the program. This reduces the apprehension.   ✳

Most residents, after two or three weeks, realize their need for help. With the settling in, they experience a novel feeling of acceptance and a consciousness that this is where they belong. By working the program, the residents learn to accept where they have come from and begin to realize the essential steps of recovery which are necessary to move them on towards a new course in life. For this to occur, it is imperative for each resident to confront the unresolved issues which are still lurking as part of the self-will as well as the unsettled problems which consume the person in terms of the self-pity. The recovery process entails discovering peace and happiness one-day-at-a-time, and unearthing it *in and through other people*. It consists of a dramatic movement from their destructive past where they incessantly reacted in a bleak and detrimental fashion to most of the conflicts of life. Some were simply too weak or powerless to respond to the existing challenges of life.

One staff member reports how, at Brentwood, an entirely new and hopeful view of self and family was discovered:

✳   When I came to Brentwood, I hated both my parents. When I looked at my family situation more closely, I realized that both my parents were alcoholic. I had reacted to the miserable way our whole family had been treated as children and I had to take a serious inventory of myself. I looked at my own children and my life and I discovered that I could not go on making any more excuses. So I said to myself: "Wait a minute. They weren't alcoholic because you were alcoholic. I know the difference. My own parents came from alcoholic parents. The important point for me is to be able to get on with life and to respond to situations responsibly." Today I have a choice. I can look at my parents and say "Those poor people, they didn't know it." They both died very tragic deaths *having taken their own lives*. My father was on pills and booze and my mother's death was a direct result of an overdose. I am bitter about the fact that they were alcoholic but today I do not allow this to linger in my life and consume me. Now, thanks to Brentwood, I have an insight which I never had before.

It may take time for my family to accept what happened in their lives because of my alcoholism. But in my family, I have to see the opportunity that my wife and I have been given and the one that my children are being given—a chance that my poor parents didn't have. They did *not* want to be the way they were, they simply did not have the solution. Now I have *hope* because my family has been exposed to the recovery process. I know today that I do not have to die of suicide and my family can have a better quality of life. ✳

Identifying the Individual Problems of Residents: Offering Them Support and Direction

Staff Input

Listening, asking questions and pointing to solutions is a good beginning to the identification of resident problems. The group leaders, on a one-on-one basis are able to characterize some of the more significant dimensions about the individual and these concerns are communicated through the proper channels for the benefit of the resident's overall treatment. As the residents talk and reveal themselves in group, the staff get acquainted with each individually and rather quickly ascertain what their problems are and if they have not disclosed their problems before their fifth week, they will usually do so in their inventories. The process provides for double safeguards to ensure honesty and self-disclosure. Unique problems are also identified by staff members listening to the stories of residents and by individual conversations.

Through careful observation and listening to what they *are saying* and what they *are not saying*, staff members become skillful at problem identification. They compare notes with other staff and, when possible, with the spouses and parents. New staff soon come to realize that almost all residents come with much the same problems, differing only in the unique circumstances of their lives and their relationships.

Identifying Individual Problems

Staff members are expected to distinguish problems that are common to all and those which are unique to a person by listening to their story, by observing how they interact with one another, by paying attention to their interaction with them, and by relying on other staff persons and psychological tests used at Brentwood. Fr. Paul provides the following commentary on the word unique or special:

> ✳   ...we do not want the residents to think what we have here doesn't really apply to them. That is basically what we want to break through and not allow any of them to think that they are in a special category where they don't belong or where they think that we cannot help them. This sense of being "special" is what

has isolated them all their lives. This is what prevented them from growing personally and in terms of their relationships with other people.... So the word "special" for the residents, tends to be a destructive misnomer, unhealthy and counterproductive.   ✳

But while pointing out the harmful side of the notion, Fr. Paul recognizes a positive use of "special" needs:

> ✳   We do believe that certain people who come to us may be borderline alcoholics or schizophrenic, or whatever, and that sometimes calls for psychological testing, or using the services of psychiatry in this local community...some of them may need special medical attention or special psychiatric help. Some might need resolution to matters which are more or less incidental or that are secondary to their main problem such as financial assistance but basically they are all the same stemming from the same source. Some of them may emotionally need a special type of assistance.   ✳

There is a clear distinction with Fr. Paul between the meaning of "special" and unique. Fr. Paul spends the majority of his time and effort in bringing out the uniqueness and potential in each person since this is consistent with the laws of God and the laws of nature:

> ✳   Because there are so many people (to a certain extent we are all a little different) either in terms of their talents, their personality, their likes and their dislikes, their positive attributes and their negative ones, they all have the opportunity to develop those distinctions or specialties from others. Brentwood does not deny the uniqueness of each individual but affirms this very quality in a most enriching fashion.   ✳

By rejecting the destructive element in each alcoholic, or what is referred to as "special," Brentwood attacks the root of the disease which has confounded the residents and which has led them astray in blindness and in isolation. Some people use "special" and "unique" interchangeably, whereas, at Brentwood, the term "special" alcoholic is used within the negative connotation of the term because it is felt that this takes away from the uniqueness of the person. According to Fr. Paul:

> ✳   When we talk about our principles being so basic to the program or when we cover this question of uniqueness we are also referring to personal fulfillment, freedom, acceptance and the person's ability to accept other people where they are at and not to put everybody in the same category. When we do categorize people as such, we are preventing them from the freedom of being them-

selves. This is the principle which we emphasize so seriously day-by-day—this is the heart of the whole program. There is no other way to respect the uniqueness of every human being except through the fulfillment, freedom, the peace and acceptance we have for one another.   ✻

Residents realize by the time they get to Brentwood that the alcoholism is no longer the actual drinking or drugging. It is felt that if only the alcohol were confronted, the whole treatment to this approach would simply be superficial. By dealing with the more compelling aspects of a person's life, a greater penetration can be made into the heart of their psycho-social and spiritual dysfunctioning. The actual issue of alcohol and drug use can be *nipped in the bud* when peace and serenity are brought to a person. Most of them have a multitude of problems and the dope or the booze can be traced to self-will and self-pity which are manifested in such problematic areas as *arrogance, hardheartedness, overindulgence, denial, anger, malice, bitterness, pugnacity, deceit, egotism, condescension, envy,* and *spiritual laziness.* Alcoholics, being engrossed in most of these, are preoccupied in the self-centered proclivities of life. They are closed and don't know either how to deal with people or how to share their lives with them.

Some have failed to look after different responsibilities which they had, (i.e., not paying the rent, evading eviction notices, dodging court orders, and so on). Some have been in trouble vocationally, others have experienced family and marriage breakdown. Each person has been affected differently by their own parents, their spouse, their children, their job, their marriage and their numerous other relationships. Brentwood distinctively deals with each one of them.

Though some of the specific issues might vary, most of the residents come with the same problem. According to Fr. Paul, there is a common factor which is reflective of all alcoholics:

✻   Basically the disease is the same in every alcoholic. Some of the details, in terms of their experiences, might differ but the so called disease is the same whether male or female, young or old. It takes a certain amount of experience, training and ability to be able to pinpoint some of the problems or difficulties that they might be having because they often differ from the ones they think they have or that seem to be before their eyes. Normally, when it is something that they themselves don't realize, it differs from what they think is their problem and it takes experience coupled with a certain amount of self-assurance for staff to skillfully recognize and accurately detect this.

So with my background and experience, we quite often can pinpoint critical issues immediately and accurately. I have a certain ability which I have developed over the years and I have very little difficulty on a regular basis with people who come to my office to seek help in identifying their disease or in recognizing what steps need to be taken toward recovery.   *

Differences

Brentwood attempts to see each person as "unique," but also as someone who has a disease which has common characteristics. According to Fr. Paul:

*   I see them all as basically similar since the disease is very much the same. Except you can have a severity of problems in the alcoholic very much similar to the severity of problems in any kind of disease or weakness, whether it be mental retardation or any physical handicap where one can be more seriously afflicted than others. So many experience much more severity in terms of violence or they have suffered to a greater extent through sexual abuse.

Some people in terms of personality are much more prone to anger or ambition than others. The basic problems are there and perhaps they have allowed their weaknesses or defects to grow deeper and stronger because of their personality but we never run into someone whom we don't understand or who confuses us to the extent that we haven't yet experienced such an individual in our twenty-five years of involvement. It might just be in the extent of how they lived or carried out their actions.   *

The disease is experienced differently if people are teenagers, single, married, retired, in a second or third marriage or if they are living common-law. The older residents have a lot more pain to deal with, pain which they have caused themselves and other people. The hard-core street alcoholics, for example, present a remarkably different problem because they have learned to survive by being street-wise, a "survival of the fittest" type of mentality. There are those who, for the most part, have a half-decent job and a good family but whose lives, for one reason or another, are just coming apart. They can't see their way clear to meet expectations as a spouse, a parent or a friend, but are still struggling and trying to make ends meet. Native people and some ethnic groups have particular characteristics which are specific to their culture. Though each have their own unique personalities, it has been the Brentwood experience that a fair number have broken hearts, shattered spirits and a defeating sense of self-pity by the time they arrive. Determining how far each resident has deteriorated as to the severity of self-pity and self-will is seen as mainly a matter of degree.

Brentwood sees alcoholics as having *pushed* people out of their lives because they have a *"people problem"*. What staff members take into consideration is their *individuality* and the prospect of their being able to maximize their potential. Ultimately, their strengths have to be ascertained. As one staff member optimistically relates:

✻ No matter how shattered and broken they may be, practicing alcoholics or recovering alcoholics do not lose their *individuality*. God simply *does not* run out of gifts to give us but is abundant in what He gives each one of us. It is just like in sobriety, everybody wants to clone Fr. Paul or be like some other recovered alcoholic whom they greatly admire, but this is not meant to be. God has given each one of us a gift to be uniquely who we are. We have a responsibility to be the best we can be. If anyone tries to be "me" they can only be the second best "me."

It can be compared to the *living waters*, the nurturance is there for the asking. I think what I respect the most today is the unrepeatable gift of everyone's uniqueness, including my own. Before, I was trying to pigeonhole everybody and get them all thinking "my way." I wasn't happy unless they were doing my will and doing things my way. I made people move to my advantage. I destroyed people and ruined their lives. I could only be with people if it was to my selfish advantage. I can see it differently now and people are not just pawns to be moved at will like in a chess game. Accepting people as they are is so important and my task is to work to bring out that uniqueness very much like the unique beauty of a rose. In the past I would trample on people because I didn't have any respect for anyone. Now I have a deeper regard for the "seed" that is inside each person. Today my responsibility is to respect that each human being comes from God and is not something to be tampered with. I know that there is something in each one placed there by God and my task is to foster that person's growth and aliveness. I see each person as being on a journey towards God and I have to "be there" to help that person on his or her way.

I know that when I now meet a new person, if I am their friend, and if I work in harmony with that individual, I can, with the help of fellowship, bring this person into full bloom and this person then will be as "*un-alike*" me in so many ways and yet will be so much "*like*" me in other ways. This is possible because now they have a uniqueness that they will never forget. They will clearly remember me because I enabled them to "*find themselves*" again, their true self. I have a great deal of optimism when I see a new person entering the recovery process. ✻

Individual Program Plans

Individual program plans are made depending on the individual's personal and family situation, their work status or any issues dealing with relationships, abuse, parental problems, or children problems. Brentwood makes a concerted effort to deal with the major issues surrounding a person's life, particularly those which impinge upon their effective functioning at home and in the community. More serious issues are dealt with by other helping professionals in the community.

Each person has individual issues other than substance abuse that need to be worked on, whether intolerable interpersonal relationships, severe sexual problems or additional unabated addictive issues. The staff take into consideration the individual personality, their manner of coping with life situations and how they interact with others. Fr. Paul explains how personalized the Brentwood experience is for each resident:

* Our staff make a very sincere and honest effort to know each individual personally in their group. In addition, they have the help of the alumni, other staff and a psychologist who at the very beginning of admission interviews everyone and is able to pinpoint specific areas of weakness or character defects. This information is given to individual leaders to help them assist each person in their group. Considering the staff we have and the way we go about this process, we have a very viable approach which is both professional and efficient in terms of helping the alcoholic on an individual level.

In effect, an Individual Program Plan starts on the very first day. A resident may be directed by a group leader to another resident who has a similar issue. In this way, a person's problem is individualized in a very caring and supportive fashion by another resident who can really identify with the pain and struggle of that resident. All the staff are qualified and take the admission policy seriously enough (four to six hours). Each individual on admission sees four or five staff including the medical and psychological department and two or three other people in addition to the director. There is enough cumulative experience and training in this group of people to assure accuracy in pinpointing the key critical elements that have to be identified for the good of each individual. *

In some instances, individual plans for residents are not all that easy to grasp or map out because recovery for the residents means that they "fit in," become "part of" and belong to a wider fellowship. In a sense it means being willing to forfeit their false sense of self.

The overall treatment plan at Brentwood includes the actual program which applies equally to all residents. The other plans complement this main plan. Detailed individual plans depend on each person's psychological test profile which determines more decisively whether that particular individual should receive professional counseling, see Fr. Paul on a continual basis, or whether or not they should be involved in an identified group for those who have been sexually abused, those who have been sexually abusing, the "con" group, the professional group, the police group or other groups which are formed to meet emotional needs such as suicidal and psychological problems which are usually conducted by the resident psychologist. The chief diagnostician determines in consultation with Fr. Paul the precise type of program which is most suit-able for each resident. Staff will see each resident and determine her assets and liabilities and what the main problem areas are.

Through observing and listening, the staff are able to be there for residents who are prepared to let them in. When the staff provide the resident a degree of insight and peace in one area, it naturally leads to other significant areas. In their experience, the staff have discovered that as residents unfold their story about finances or their job situation that other more serious issues such as promiscuity or infidelity are usually divulged . It may even be the case where the spouse is being unfaithful. It is very much like peeling layers of onion skin, as residents discover more and more about their individual world. There is virtually no end to the process because human growth and fulfillment is at the very heart of spiritual recovery.

Determining if a Resident is "Not Going to Make It"

The process of identifying residents who will either "make it" or "not make it" can be done by competent staff, as Fr. Paul maintains:

✻   ...we can rely on the leaders in the various groups who are with the residents on a daily basis to make such an identification. They are recovered alcoholics who have been through the program themselves. They have a sense of what is needed for recovery in themselves and from their experience with hundreds of others whom they have either dealt with or whom they know as alumni. They can clearly detect if a particular resident is fitting in with the others who are making progress in their groups. Often, they can confront the specific individual involved. In addition, such matters are brought either before a group of staff, the leader or the director. There are a series of steps that must take place in each individual which provides us with a gauge as to whether or not they are going to persevere or progress in our recovery program. ✻

People get into difficulty and give signs that they will "not make it" if there is continuing apathy and if they simply refuse to participate actively in the program. Such recurrent signs as denial, withdrawal, being unable to keep commitments in regard to permission, or being unable or unwilling to show a spirit of cooperation are generally indications, according to Fr. Paul that they are not going to make it:

✻   If a resident is not progressing, it is most likely due to an unresolved issue in the past or a lack of motivation or good will. Often it can be the intensity of fear and guilt which has them locked in and which makes them frightened to move on. They shudder at the fear that they will not be able to last. Others are upset with the thought that they will have to live this way for the next twenty or twenty five years and this makes them too discouraged to go on. Because they cannot consciously see themselves living this way or becoming loving and responsible in the near future, they more or less decide to leave.   ✳

Although such determination is possible, Kay Ryan identifies the complexity of determining who will or will not make it:

✳   It is difficult to say and you can't really judge them prematurely because it varies with each situation. I heard of a woman who had hardly made any progress until three weeks before graduation and today she is just terrific. For some it just takes longer because they have been hurt more than others. Some need more mending because the wounds are much more profound and less accessible to change and modification.   ✳

If residents are not prepared *"to ask, listen and do what they are told"* and if the willingness is not there, it becomes less and less probable that they will have the ingredients necessary to make the program work. Residents determine rather easily for themselves whether or not they are going to "botch" things up. Some residents could be in their tenth, twelfth or thirteenth week and suddenly they see the real value in what is being said, in terms of the opportunity to change their lives. Some go right up to their very last week and say: "Oh my God. Now I understand!" And everything comes together in their mind and in their heart and they now want it more convincingly than ever.

A staff member might conceivably see a resident and say: "Wow! Do they have a long way to go." And all of a sudden, some residents show a remarkable recovery and insight in their lives. As one staff member warns:

✳   A caution needs to be exercised, nonetheless, because some people may show no willingness up to the sixth week and suddenly, something happens where they *"turn it around"*. So we have to be very careful and avoid a premature judgment that might close a person off permanently. The fact is that most of them have never had the incentive to demonstrate any willingness or motivation. Why should we think that in a couple of weeks they are going to willingly cooperate at the drop of a hat? They may have a bit of willingness but if they are going to rebel, it is most likely that it will be here at Brentwood where the rebellion will occur. If you go along with them and give them the benefit of the doubt, they may just "grab it" and be able to turn it around. So it requires careful discretion in determining the proper timing as to when to effectively confront.   ✳

Staff, in most instances, get a fairly good sense of the residents' ability to grasp the program in about their fifth week. They can do this by observing how well or how poorly they have taken to their inventories, by the quality or the lack of quality of their participation in the group and their overall attitude and behavior on the premises. As the residents develop the ability to submit voluntarily to someone else's will and to do what they are told, (i.e., their name not constantly being brought forth because they are not doing what they're told, not doing their job, or not carrying out their chores) chances are that they are going to make it. As the program is in progress, the staff also observe the willingness of the resident to be "part of" and their acceptance of the word "No." If a resident is complying with the rules and acknowledging the basic principles of the program, then the "No" should be sufficient and does not have to be explained. If they are still obstinately in their self-will, then it is most likely that they will still be preoccupied with the self. In their disease, they will try to rationalize most things.

As can be seen, one of the major determining factors for failure of residents to make it on program is an obstinate "self-will" and a persistent "negative attitude." If they cannot function in the protective environment of Brentwood with the caring and support offered, it is unlikely that they will be successful on the outside where life can be more demanding and unbearable. It is equally true that if they are unable to bend to the will of others who are trying to help them, particularly the staff, it is unlikely they will be able to yield to the legitimate needs of their spouse, their parents or their supervisors at work when they leave the program.

When staff are in communication with a resident, they can tell when they are not getting anything back from them and if there is no change taking place in the resident. When residents are not complying to the spirit of the fellowship or when they remain closed or refuse to be "part of" the home group, it is unlikely that they can succeed. When they keep a very negative attitude and remain withdrawn at a point when they should be more involved and invested in the growing process, it is doubtful that they can prosper from the program. Are they getting into the jobs that they have been assigned? Are they getting up in the morning or are they refusing to do what they are told? Do they seem to be taking part in things? How shallow are they in their interactions? Are they getting deeper into their own issues? Are they sharing with the other resident, seeking out one-on-ones? Are they demonstrating a lack of cooperation? Are they cutting corners? Does their program lack "honest to goodness" sharing? Do they continue to be negative, hostile and rebellious? Do they have a difficult time sharing and do they look despondent and unhappy? In the Brentwood terminology, are they self-willing it? It may be difficult to determine these factors immediately upon their admission on program, due to their fear and insecurity. Nonetheless, if the self-will and the self-pity persists well into the program, then it is obvious that they are having some difficulty adjusting. Staff members can detect from day to day when residents are causing trouble on program or when they are not fully invested in the social activities of the day.

Relapse recovery takes hold when the alcoholic is willing to change his or her life so that he or she can live according to the principles of the program. It is sometimes impossible to do anything for those in relapse who are unwilling to see how badly things have gotten and who remain blind to the help they need. Unfortunately, some still have to go out and practice the disease further and have a "bigger fall" before they can realize how badly they need to turn their lives around. Unfortunately, some do not make it.

Brentwood's Recidivism (Relapse) Rate

The word "recidivism" means "relapse." Most alcoholics have relapses and in the field of recovery this process is referred to as "recidivism." Brentwood's recidivism rate is approximately twenty-five percent, meaning that 25 of every hundred residents will relapse at some time. But many of those who relapse return for further treatment: there can be as many as seventeen out of 167 repeaters on average in any given week. For example, one group leader had five people who had been at Brentwood for a period of time. Somewhere in their forth or fifth week they left and had come back. The same group leader also had two people who graduated, went out and came back. If the recidivism rate refers to return of those who actually graduated, the recidivism rate is very low. But the percentage increases if the recidivism rate refers to those who have only been at Brentwood for a very short period of time—anywhere from two weeks to eight weeks—and return. These people may have heard something, seen something or wanted something which they missed in their first attempt and they came back to Brentwood to get the help they needed. One staff member aptly put it this way:

> ✻   The ones who have to come back are the ones who "weren't coming back" once they graduated. Those who are coming back and staying in tune with the family, the team, keeping a positive outlook on life are less prone to relapse. They have the peace, the openness and the honesty and they are practicing their program because they have other people in their lives.   ✻

Fr. Paul maintains that it is difficult to determine Brentwood's recidivism rate because people in the field define relapse differently and use different criteria to assess when it actually occurs. According to Fr. Paul:

> ✻   I do not like such statistics because nobody looks at results the way we do at Brentwood. To be here for twenty-eight days or to be here ninety days has no meaning to me in regards to data

or to measurements of whether one is having results that are beneficial or not. At Brentwood, we do not believe in looking at any statistics under three years from the time a resident initiates the recovery process. The reason for this is that in order for the program to have its maximum impact and in order for it to have any lasting value it is essential that the residents who are working their program properly should have the time to turn their lives around and to live as effective human beings with the others.

Under three to five years, we are being rather naive to think that the full and tangible effects of recovery are actually happening or that it has thoroughly "kicked in" to the lives of alcoholics in a way that they can be more fully human. The disease is so ingrained in them that it takes three to four years for them to even begin to scratch the surface and get to the core where life becomes enjoyable, where recovery becomes a way of life and where they not only believe in it or talk about it but they are able to live it. They acknowledge that this way of life is rewarding and worthwhile.   ✳

As mentioned above, Brentwood's rate has been calculated at 25% when measured over a brief period, as most programs are measured. However when measured over the longer period of 3–5 years, it is much lower.

Staff Attitude Towards "Repeaters"

In terms of "repeaters," staff try to talk directly with each resident involved and find out what happened and why they stopped coming back. From there, they take the necessary steps to assist the individual with his or her recovery. Staff members have been exposed to the principles of relapse counseling.

The belief of Brentwood regarding members who relapse and return has been summed up by Fr. Paul:

✳   The whole issue of alcoholism and the process of recovery entails relapse. At Brentwood all residents are taken seriously whether they arrive for the first time or for the twentieth time. What each alcoholic needs is love, forgiveness, self-worth and fellowship. Some are not ready to surrender to the disease and subsequently are not able to make any progress. When they are prepared to submit, to confide and to consult, then sobriety is possible. Only then can they find inner peace and joy in their lives.   ✳

Not everyone is expected to get the program perfectly the first time around. Most staff members welcome the repeaters back gladly and make every effort to be open to them and provide a supportive base though at the same time they have to be both cautious and demanding in terms of their expectations. Some take longer to return, some people need more help than others because of the seriousness of their relapse. If a resident returns after a fall, the staff respect the courage they have mustered to return for help considering they most likely failed because they were not ready or they obviously missed something in their program. It is considered imperative at this juncture that they make a much more concerted effort to "grasp" the program. Some staff members were repeaters themselves and are happy to see that those who come back can now get the help they need.

Far from being disturbed by the presence of repeaters, Fr. Paul has a very positive, welcoming attitude:

✳   It is a healthy thing for us to have "repeaters." It is very difficult for an alcoholic to make a complete attitude change or to alter a whole way of life. It means moving from being a very selfish irresponsible person to being a very caring, loving, responsible person. We would be very naive if we thought that the majority of residents would get the program on their first day out following their graduation.

So the miracle is that many do grasp it the first time around. The fact that those who have relapsed would come back is encouraging because if they failed out there and still want to return to the place where they originally failed, it must be a good indication that they believe in the program and that they still want the help from the same spot in which they floundered.

It is also a healthy thing for those on program to have repeaters present (twenty-five or thirty on a regular basis) because in their honesty they tell the present group of people on program, "Don't do what we did because we watered it down." The residents are not only getting these guidelines and the encouragement of how to go about the program from the point of view of the staff and the alumni, but more importantly they are also getting it from repeaters with whom they are presently on program. This, in a sense, is a very valuable experience. Often as a collegial friend to friend, or on a buddy to buddy level, they can often influence the people on program more than staff or alumni.   ✳

Some staff members believe that:

✳   Repeaters need to be treated with care and with patience. They need to face the consequences of their actions and of their slipping away. We can share it with them as can others. Heavy confrontation with repeaters has not proven all that successful and is not condoned.   ✳

Dealing with Relapse

Staff members, for the most part, feel a need to sustain a more firm and uncompromising stance with relapse victims. They don't let them get away with anything. Mainly because some have been at Brentwood before and they try to slip through again. The staff, being aware of this, are more alert to people with such a recalcitrant attitude and attempt to make sure that these repeaters follow the rules to a 'T' because it is obvious that they have missed something along the line in their previous attempt at recovery. They have to start back at square one. The staff realize that they already have something by virtue of the fact that they were at Brentwood before and something *obviously rubbed off* for them to want to return again. Apparently, what they had they did not fully lose; they temporarily shelved it. Now they can pick it up and use it. They are placed back on a full program of usually twenty-eight days and put into the mainstream of the program. In fact, repeaters are treated very much the same as the new person on program with the exception that they begin to write inventories almost immediately.

In more or less exceptional instances, some relapse victims have returned five or six times. The program is geared to get them to "fit in" immediately and to write up their inventories straightaway so as to determine where they went wrong. The first inventory will provide a fairly accurate indication of where the relapse occurred and why. When they get honest as to whether they drank or smoked up, the staff try to pick them up and get them back on the positive side. With gentle understanding, the staff attempt to determine in what way the self-will seeped in. Normally, the staff will immediately "hit" them more directly as to their lack of program.

On occasion, some residents must go to AA and show that they have some willingness to practice the Brentwood principles before being readmitted. Because Brentwood is aware of the needs of repeaters, it has initiated a training program for the staff in recognizing and treating relapse situations.

Fr. Paul, just like good parents with their child, doesn't let repeaters take their relapse lightly. He believes it is important to be *loving*, yet firm and exacting. He does not provide any preferential treatment for repeaters that would feed the disease further. In his words:

    *   The story of the Prodigal Son has always been one of the foundations of fellowship and recovery of the alcoholic and is particularly applicable to the issue of relapse. By accepting them back where they have the opportunity to experience once again this forgiveness, where they are not ridiculed, they are not put in a "special" alcoholic category. It gives staff and alumni an opportunity to practice their principles of acceptance and forgiveness for these people. This gives the people who have relapsed an opportunity to experience the truth of these principles of love, forgiveness, acceptance and the warmth of the fellowship. It subsequently gives the people on the program the opportunity to accept them. The bottom line is that just as it is a healthy thing for an individual to be accepted again in the family if one of the children relapses, leaves home or is asked to leave home and is away for a number of years, the Brentwood family receives him or her back and there is a lot of joy.   ✳

Determining the Nature and Severity of the Relapse
Fr. Paul explains:

✳   Repeaters have a lot of trust. The fact that they have already been at Brentwood and have previously experienced a lot of help, is evidence that they would not have come back had they not had an inherent trust for the program. Therefore, from day one, they have the ability of being much more honest and open with us when they come back a second or third time than the first time. They are all received with open arms and are all made to feel "fully welcomed." Because of the honesty, it is very easy to pinpoint how serious the relapse has been.   ✳

Relapse is a serious business. Those who return all require careful attention. Brentwood believes that a relapse is a relapse whether it is caused by one drink or ten drinks. Fundamentally, the self-pity and the self-will have taken over again. It is important to look at how serious the attitude problem is and the underlying area which the repeater is refusing to examine. The overriding concern is that the repeaters may not have another chance "to make it" if they keep slipping since alcoholism and addiction can ultimately be fatal.

It is rather serious for a member who has had a touch of the program and has chosen to throw it away. Some, who leave Brentwood have a rough time to get situated, to get a job and so forth. Staff can be more understanding in these circumstances because of the fact that they were "down" to start off with. But the ones who are on their feet and then throw it away again present a frightening situation which requires careful attention.

There are a host of warning signs which Brentwood takes into consideration when looking at the issue of relapse. If they have a wife and family and go back to drinking, then there are more serious aspects which require primary attention. The staff have to look at the marital situation, the job situation and the extent of damage that has transpired since the person last came to Brentwood and the person's attitude and disposition toward recovery. What is the severity of the family setting? How much has the family been disrupted? How long has it been damaged and how long has the person been in relapse? How long have they been out? How long has the person been dry? How serious was the drinking and drugging? What kind of trouble did they get into? How frequently did they "use" again? How long have they been depressed or in relapse?

How serious are their family problems or their home situation? Did they just lose their job? As one staff member remarked. "One just prays to God that those who return will 'hang in' and want it for themselves."

Relapse has to be considered in light of the time it takes for the person to get honest about the incident or series of incidents which led to the relapse. What was the amount and length of time involved? Was it every day for a week, for example? Was it one beer, or two or three beers? What were the real reasons behind the drinking or drugging? How faithfully are they prepared to come back and "work the program"? It is usually something else other than the drinking or the drugging that is the real underlying problem in relapse. The severity of the relapse is influenced by the amount of time they have been practicing, whether a few days, a few weeks, a few months or a few years. It is time and proportion to time that is the integral aspect here.

Former residents who relapse but haven't been back in ten months, could have a two-year relapse before they seek help. Some miss their former friends at Brentwood and have a desire to be connected with them again. It is felt that the longer they are away, the more difficult it is to return. And sometimes, those who have the most difficulty in coming back are the ones who have not taken a single drink, the "dry drunks" who have been holding a resentment against another person at home, at work or at Brentwood.

Alcoholics tend to carry resentments for a variety of reasons. They may have been compelled to do something in the past that was against their will and had to "kowtow" to their parents, spouse, the boss or someone else. Some may have a resentment against Fr. Paul or a staff member because they thought they were coerced to do something or they felt "stepped upon." Holding these things as a grudge, they end up very much like a *"dry drunk"* with all the wretched characteristics which that entails.

In a good number of cases, repeaters have basically failed to be honest with their program the first time round. Essentially, they are back because they did not really surrender in the first place—*an important ingredient of sobriety and recovery.*

Brentwood, Suicide and God's Mercy

Staff members believe that there is a high percentage of the deceased people's names posted on the front plaque of Brentwood who have committed suicide. It is also felt that their fatal gesture could easily have been predicted when one reflects on the attitude and disposition of these people prior to their death. Most likely they were so sick that they could not handle life any longer. It is very difficult for staff to deal with the issue of suicide since most of them are usually very angry with the person who dies and, in some instances annoyed at themselves for not having been able to prevent it. Sometimes alcoholics do not know what causes them to be so angry and depressed. As one staff member remarks:

✳   When somebody said that I was alcoholic I didn't realize that it involved my being blocked emotionally and socially because of all the hurt inside. I didn't know how to share my feelings. I had an empty feeling inside. I remember that sometimes suicide seemed the better choice. That's how badly I felt inside. Brentwood gave me a new lease on life, where now I do not need to resort to suicide.   ✳

While still disturbed, some staff members seriously ask themselves: "Could I have done something differently that would have changed the situation?" Some group leaders become disturbed if a resident leaves the Brentwood program without acquiring self-worth. They feel that they may not have done their job sufficiently for this individual: that he or she wasn't adequately heard or that somehow, something went dreadfully wrong. Some leaders always keep hoping that such an individual will ultimately return and convey to them: "Ah, I simply *did not* hear what Fr. Paul was saying. I didn't hear because I wasn't open to receive it. I was there with two ears but I just didn't hear." One staff member sadly recalls:

✳   I had one individual, who was here on program, accused of some pretty violent things. He was sent to another facility in Toronto, where he stayed for about six months, was released, and they declared that it was an impossible feat for him to have been able to do these things. When he came to Brentwood he let me know that he was going to kill himself. I tried to encourage him to talk to Fr. Paul, to talk to his lawyer and to talk to his psychiatrist and to get honest. He wouldn't do this and, as a result, he eventually took his own life.

Another chap came here with a sex problem. I tried to encourage him to get it out with the director, Fr. Paul and with the police. Instead, he drove his car into a transport truck. I had another individual who was involved with incest and I encouraged him to go to Fr. Paul to find some self-worth and to help him recognize what he couldn't accept readily. Unfortunately, he hung himself. One particular fellow, some may refer to it as an accident, walked in front of a car. He just couldn't forgive himself for what he had done. None of those who have committed suicide were able to forgive themselves for what they had done. No one could assure them that they were *forgiven*. Consequently, their only *solution* was *death*. The unfortunate thing is that the suicide could have been avoided. I myself came to Brentwood not feeling good about myself but I was able to find the forgiveness. I accepted forgiveness from other people, from God and most importantly—I forgave myself.   ✳

Staff members often feel enraged at a suicide victim because they themselves have felt the same desperate urge to take their own life at one time or another. They grieve that the others did not make it, because the victims cheated themselves and they short-changed significant others by not looking at what they left behind. One staff member laments:

✳ They're the ones who thought they were suffering the most but it is the children or the mother or father who have to live on with the pain. They were so caught up in themselves that they couldn't be there for someone else. They failed to see what effect their death would have on others. ✳

One staff member was bothered for a while by a fatal incident that occurred only recently yet now, in retrospect, has less regret:

✳ I wonder sometimes what I could have done to have prevented it. I feel an element of discouragement in the fact that it happened in the first place. I checked myself out very thoroughly: "Could I have done more for this fellow? *Yes*, I could have, but he *wouldn't let me*". I know that I did everything that I possibly could in my power for that person unless I would have harbored him, sheltered him, put him under my wing, or even have imprisoned him to keep him from hurting himself. I was as good a friend to him as he would allow me to be without imposing my will on him. When such an individual's self-will is so strong, there comes a point where a person's hands are tied and there is not really anything anyone can do if he or she doesn't want to listen to you. It is also important to know that we are not God and that there are some people who do not want the recovery or the life line. ✳

For some staff members, the issue of suicide brings them back in time to the point where they themselves didn't want to live. They are therefore empathic to people who are still suicidal. They desperately want "to be there" for them and to help them. One staff member demonstrates her irritation and exasperation with words of magnanimity and consolation:

✳ This disturbs and upsets me because it has actually occurred to women who had been in my group. I get mad at myself and ask: "Should I have seen something extra in their lives? Was there something which I missed and that I could have prevented? Could I have reached out my hand and have avoided this fatality?" It plays on me. It annoys me terribly. ✳

There are several alumni who, before they came to Brentwood, were suicidal. One alumna relates her gratitude for the program:

✳   I made several suicide attempts before I came to Brentwood. Today the idea of suicide no longer crosses my mind. Brentwood has turned my whole life around in every area. I have been with Brentwood for six years. I have never touched a drink nor have I done any drugs in that time. I have learned to deal with life and its issues one-day-at-a-time. Today I can rejoice because I see life in a healthier dimension and I have a freedom and peace which I never had before.   ✳

Another person relates a compelling story of desperation and despair prior to Brentwood:

✳   Before I came here, I had a very wretched existence. My life was in shambles—in the depths of despair. I had been brutally raped at the age of fifteen. I had an unwanted pregnancy at sixteen which was kept hushed up. My child died soon after. I was a victim of my father's alcoholism and his cruelty. My father warned me that I was never to mention a word about the baby ever again but I was to cover it all up instead. When I think of it, I had repressed all the fear, anger and resentment of what had been done to me. I had my past so buried, yet, I unknowingly carried it with me all these years. It wasn't until I came to Brentwood that I was able to free myself of it. I always had a very negative self-image and I constantly put myself down. Life for me was miserable and un-manageable. I covered all my guilt and disappointment to the point where I was barely existing. Life was a drudgery, an endurance test every step of the way. My life was so full of gloom, desperation and discouragement that I just wanted to die. I made several serious attempts at suicide. At one point a priest administered the last rites since they thought I was going to die. I felt like a "no-body." Life had absolutely no meaning for me at all. I could experience no joy or freedom in life.

When I came to Brentwood I was so desperate that I still wanted to do myself in by taking an overdose of sleeping pills. I asked Fr. Paul if there was any hope for me. His words of encouragement sparked a ray of promise for me and gave me the courage and motivation to start, in a feeble way, on my road to recovery. As I practiced the principles, I could feel a cloud lifting which allowed me to feel more joy and peace. Those who know me can attest to the remarkable change which has occurred. I took on a whole new dimension to life. I suddenly developed a sense of purpose. I had a reason to live. I became convinced that I could make a valuable contribution to society and that I could "appreciate me" once more.

In my past life I spent most of my time "getting" whatever I could from others. Now I can give and it comes back to me one hundredfold. I no longer feel that sordid sense of gloom and depletion. I always have energy in abundant supply not only for myself but also for others. In my old way of life, I was never happy because my life was always one-sided. It was always what I could get and never what I could give. What I was doing was all so selfish. I was brought up with nothing and my whole life I felt worthless. This negativity was thrown in my face wherever I turned. Brentwood has given me so much confidence that my present job is a "real reward" which I appreciate so very much.   ✳

Alumni have difficulty resolving the issue of suicide when it occurs. It is felt, to some extent, that suicide can be totally dishonest and actually a cowardly way of avoiding personal responsibility. At the time of the suicide they probably don't think there is another way to escape from their problems. In their denial, they reject the good way of life which Brentwood offered to them. Though the staff detest seeing someone make such a fatal and catastrophic decision, they have no alternative but to accept it. A person close to them or even a relative could make the same choice. As one person laments:

> ✳   My daughter is going through strife right now and she could reject the truth in her life and this frightens me. I realize that it is within the freedom of individuals to choose suicide but I simply hate to see this as an alternative. It is truly the difference between self-will and God's will. The decision is self-destructive.   ✳

The anguish for staff is in not being able to reach them. It is not that the staff didn't try but the victims were not open to doing anything about their condition. The victims of suicide are the extreme example, those who could not or would not take the *risk* to be completely open and honest in order to become "part of" the group.

It is disheartening to acknowledge the loss, through suicide, of former Brentwood residents who were involved with the program. The victims outstandingly did one thing wrong—*they stayed away*. It shouldn't have had to happen. They failed to keep contact with the fellowship. They chose to die rather than to live and, in the process, gave up on life and themselves. If a person self-wills it, the inevitable consequences are life-threatening. The Brentwood recovery process works if one has the *willingness to come back* and to stick with the honesty. Fr. Paul offers some very clear insights in this regard:

> ✳   Years ago the whole issue of suicide was a concern to us and it would create a real sense of guilt for us and we would be asking ourselves: "Where did we fail? Could we have prevented it?" Each one of us sort of examines in our minds what possibly went wrong. Most of us as alcoholics have experienced the thought and feeling of committing suicide, of ending it, so much so that we have come to believe that it is part of the disease. We realize that if we don't

attend to our disease and take care of it that it will ultimately
destroy not only others but ourselves. The vast majority will not
carry out a suicidal threat, though every alcoholic has those feelings of ending life, either their own or someone else's. That is part
of the feelings that alcoholics experience day in and day out when
they reach a certain point. So, knowing this and having experienced similar inclinations so frequently on our own part, we can
all accept it more and not be so horrified or startled by it, knowing
that it could have happened and most likely would have happened
if we had not done something about it. This is our belief, it is our
philosophy and we emphasize this in our teaching with our people.
To change one's life around, a person has to feel a sense of belonging with other people.   ✳

One alumnus explains:

✳   In terms of God's mercy and compassion, I believe that God
has a plan for every one of us. We are all a message to the other
person. I believe ultimately that suicide is what ensues if I cannot
accept the forgiveness, if I cannot accept doing what I am told in
order to receive the forgiveness by sharing. If I fail to do the right
responsible things, if I fail to act according to God's will, there are
inevitable consequences.   ✳

A Glimpse of God's Mercy and Compassion

In his own theological training and in his experience with the
alcoholic, Fr. Paul has come to a deepening awareness of God's eternal
and ever-present mercy for those who have committed suicide. He states:

✳   Human beings are pale examples of God's love, of God's forgiveness and of God's mercy. We experience through the fellowship
how human beings can love, forgive and accept and so this to me
just emphasizes how, day in and day out, that if we can do this
with one another, and considering that we are very weak, then it
is much clearer and more convincing to me of God's love and mercy,
because if we can show it and we are pale imitations of God, then
how much more can God do it? The vast majority of residents by
the time they come in here have little or no faith either in one
another or in God. By experiencing the love and forgiveness of one
another many of them can come to believe in God's love and forgiveness. One can almost be an eternal optimist when it comes to
God's love since the Brentwood philosophy is that God's love and
forgiveness comes in and through one another. God works through
people.   ✳

One alumna affirms this view in her own reflection:

✻   I have thought of this somewhat. I feel deep down that God in His mercy automatically forgives them. I believe that those who have committed suicide were so far gone in the disease that they were not fully responsible for what they did. I don't question this because in my mind I feel that when they commit suicide they go temporarily insane. It is like they are not themselves. I am convinced that God's compassion and mercy is greater than his justice. Some people simply cannot live life. They are not strong enough to make it. For some, they have been so much into their disease that they have been lost. So God most likely has clemency on them in the last moment. God is very forgiving.

I believe and am hopeful that God's mercy is greater than his wrath or condemnation. I believe that the alcoholic at the last minute may have been so caught up in her disease that she was powerless to distinguish. I am convinced of this today with all my heart.

When our beliefs coincide with God's, it is marvelous to see how our lives are changed for the better. I felt this previously when I was doing good things in my life, but when I started to be selfish, self-centered and egotistical, where I was hurting so many people, this is when my life started to really deteriorate and I couldn't find any peace, joy or happiness, no matter where I looked for it. I try and intercede with God through prayer for people who take their lives. I can be very compassionate and understanding towards people. Just as God has been forgiving to me, so I can be forgiving and benevolent to others. I couldn't love others until I received God's love. I know that today and I believe this with all my heart. It wasn't until I took on a *healing heart,* a heart integrally related to a unified act of self-fulfillment. My heart became united with God, with people and with the community. I want to share my energy and life-force with others.   ✻

Another person remarks:

✻   It is very sad when you hear about it because the act of suicide is so completely unnecessary. Had they stayed and continued with the program it could have been avoided. Everything they needed was available here at Brentwood had they only reached out. It comes across as a wasted decision which is ill-timed and unfortunate. Suicide is one last attempt at bringing about a final solution. I view it as both the final attack of the disease and also the capitulation of the person, the surrender of the person to the disease. Rarely, do people take their own lives solely for altruistic motives. My hope is that at long last they may be released from the effects of this disease and in God's mercy and compassion find peace in their souls.   ✻

Women Alcoholics: Similarities and Differences

It has been the Brentwood experience that women and men, to some extent, have similar problems with the disease. Recognizing the commonality of the disease, there are some qualities which are similar in both men and women, since neither know how to express their feelings or how to share their pain. Whether male or female, self-will and self-pity are the same. Though the disease is the same in both, men seem to have a more difficult time expressing feelings and women seem to suffer more deeply. Fr. Paul characterizes the resemblances while noting some marked distinctions:

> *   There are some similarities because women suffer the same hurts from other people. They endure the same hang-ups, weaknesses, fears, insecurities and jealousies but in other ways they are offended even more because they take things more personally and their hurts often go deeper. The wounds and the scars are often more profound. In addition, considering that they have the children, they probably don't have a way of releasing some of the pent-up anguish like a man does when he goes into the booze or the drugs if he is not home and is out working. Women tend to be more sensitive and they are damaged more deeply and more severely. They do not have the outlet day by day to release the locked-up emotion unless they take it out on the children and then this simply adds to their guilt and confusion. Sometimes, their only way out is to use drugs or medication.   *

The distinction in women is seen in the severity of the disease. Some women, in their unwillingness to surrender to the program, seem still in iron chains suffering from their sense of guilt and loss. According to Fr. Paul:

> *   The problems of women can be deeper and more severe particularly in the area of trust. Even the women staff tend to be more suspicious and less trusting due to the fact that they have been hurt by men. It has been our experience at Brentwood that women tend to be more jealous and petty in certain matters with one another than are the men. They take their problems more personally and have more difficulty in even trusting the other women, let alone the men.   *

Some staff believe that culturally, women have a legacy of having been used and of getting their way by allowing themselves to be used, offering themselves to others in a form of surrendering their will to the will of others, particularly men. Some women prostitute themselves to get alcohol or sell their bodies to get drugs. Society with its double standards looks down upon a delinquent woman more sharply than it does a man and makes it very difficult for a woman to survive.

They may have more guilt due to their role as "mother." Women tend to be more private.

This cultural characteristic plays right into the hands of this disease. As a matter of fact, one might point to this trait as a sign of an addictive society. The problem for the woman is made all the more acute because it is believed that it is still much more difficult for a woman to admit she is an alcoholic than for a man due to the stigma that is attached.

Women have their families and their children to deal with which creates more pressing issues. They are often bogged down by these responsibilities. It is also assumed that a woman takes away more from the family when she is alcoholic and it makes the situation much more discouraging. The women who come on the program have to be concerned about their children at home. This is not usually the case with a man. In our society, everyone has a stereotype of what a woman and mother should be and very little leeway is given if she should falter from that categorization. As one staff member explains:

﹡ Society allocates roles to women which men more or less take for granted but which women must deal with when they are on program at Brentwood. The men could be the "fallen" drunk, they could be picking up women and it would be seen as "cool" somehow. If a woman is drunk, she is immediately labeled. I know, because I was one of those fallen women. Men in society can get away with almost anything in comparison to women who are labeled "tramps" and "no good." Though things are better today, there are still overlays of the "double standard" in operation today. We tend to be more difficult on women than on men. ﹡

Further, it is believed by Brentwood staff that a male is very much compartmentalized in his thinking process whereas a woman, when she is injured, tends to experience it more devastatingly and more deeply with every fiber of her being. Women are taught and allowed to feel more deeply than men. Therefore their wounds are deeper and more penetrating, and recovery is longer because of the intensity of their emotions. When a woman falls, she tends to fall harder, and some may have been shattered and crushed by a deleterious alcoholic relationship.

The women have been more damaged than the men because they have been hidden for so long. The sex abuse and so on is so deep that such an infliction of pain creates a special hurt of its own. Some just have a more difficult time admitting and accepting their disease and coming out of the closet about it.

Major Issues for Women Alcoholics
Thus the major need for women today is in regaining a sense of inner self-worth as distinct from external approval. According to Fr. Paul:

✳   Women have much more guilt because of the children and certainly much less self worth because of the values of our present-day-society. A lot of the thinking is that women get their self-worth, not by being mothers and wives, but by having jobs and careers in society. This was not always so, but in today's society very few people feel that they receive their self-worth just by being women, wives or mothers. They have to do something out of the home like men do to get their self-worth, validation or affirmation.

A lot of women have been sexually and physically abused while they were young and if they subsequently enter marriage and get abused either through neglect or through mental and occasionally sexual or physical abuse, some of them have less of a chance to develop any self-worth and self-respect. It is rather difficult for a young boy or a young girl to straighten their lives out after that. When this occurs at such an early age, they become trapped in such a vicious cycle that it is almost impossible for them to get out of their dilemma without the proper help and guidance.

A number of sexually abused women get into the pills as well as the drinking and end up cross-addicted. Some get promiscuous and sell themselves short in all areas of life. Many develop, as a result, a very poor father image, and escape from home only to become entangled in dysfunctional relationships.   ✳

Having taken so much abuse from others, a good number of women have great difficulty in expressing anger. In the past, they were always reprimanded if they displayed any anger, so they learned to hide their feelings: they were conditioned not to display any wrath or displeasure. Some even feared that they might kill somebody with their anger. As one alumna remarked: "There can be so much bottled-up hostility that a tremendous fear takes over us: fear that if we let go of this anger that somebody is going to die or be seriously maimed."

Brentwood's Involvement of the Family

Brentwood has always involved family from the very beginning. In the early '70s Fr. Paul realized that wives needed help because they had been affected by their husbands' sickness: some elements of the disease had rubbed off on them. According to Fr. Paul:

✳   ...families have been helped in finding lodging or food and some initial assistance, in the reconstructing of their lives, the reconstitution of their marriages and in bringing them to some semblance of happiness.   ✳

Some wives who were not alcoholic but whose husbands were, came to Brentwood for direction. Many had such unfortunate experiences in their marriage that they could not imagine their husbands eventually coming home and starting again where they left off because there was so much hate there and so much damage. So they asked Fr. Paul for meetings for these women. As one woman hesitantly describes:

> ✳   At first I was fearful of the meetings because I was afraid to show myself. I was afraid to share things because I was not sure if it would get back to my husband and create more tension in the home. I didn't know what to expect, but once I went to them I felt so good inside.   ✳

The first group for women alcoholics started with six women. From January to October, 1976, Brentwood had a group of women on the program who came once a week and sat in on the groups and most of these women today are still sober. They were women who wanted additional help from Brentwood.

Staff and Family Involvement

Group leaders try to find out as much as they can about each resident and their relationship with their spouse and children and try to bring the family closer together. The residents are encouraged to let their spouses know about the meetings that are available for them and for the children. They are informed how alcoholism is a family disease and that if they are going to *grow* as a family, they have to *grow together*.

Sometimes it is discovered in the intake process that there are serious problems indicating the need to forbid a resident from contacting family members, or the family indicates that they are not ready for contact with a resident. When this happens the staff, in consultation with Fr. Paul, decide in each case whether a resident should be forbidden to make such a contact. According to Fr. Paul:

> ✳   We have some basic rules that we follow. The leaders in conjunction with me will view each case individually and decisions are made on what we mutually believe is the right thing for any particular individual, for the family and for her program of recovery.   ✳

A "resident-no-contact" order is mostly given when the problems at home are too serious, when ordered from the courts in the form of a peace bond, or when there has been evidence of abuse.

The Family Reaction when a Loved One Enters Program for Treatment

There are usually one of two reactions for wives whose husbands come on program. Either acceptance or rejection. By the time a resident comes on program a good number of families want to have nothing to do with the person: they have pretty well "had it." The wife and the children in futile desperation have been exposed and subjected to antagonism, terror and outrage and they, too, are in need of recovery. It is believed that ninety percent of the partners of the residents have been *seriously* jeopardized by the disease and its effect. Many are angry and frightened. Many attend support groups and find help for themselves. There may be denial and hesitation because they are not sure if it is going to work or not. They want change but are uncertain if they can put any faith or trust in the spouse and fear that they will have their hopes shattered again.

It is understandably embarrassing, at first, that the family problem has finally been exposed publicly. But once the wives start coming to the women's meetings, the embarrassment leaves them and they are relieved to know that things are going to get better. It is a sign of relief for the rest of the family because they may have been praying for this move towards recovery for some time. In a sense, the family is not surprised that the individual has come on program: it has been their ardent wish for a very long time that they get help. The family is now happy because they have finally found some freedom for themselves. The family feels relieved that the individual is taking steps to turn his or her life around. Most of them genuinely care and are most supportive, as a staff member remarks:

> ✳   To most spouses it is a consolation that the husband or wife is at Brentwood. The majority of them are glad that the alcoholic has finally gone for help and there now is a genuine feeling of relief. Not too many of them are confident that a successful recovery is imminent. They are not sure that Brentwood is going to make their spouse happy because a lot of them have come to the point that they do not see any hope in their marriage or their relationship. They are just glad that there is going to be some reduction in the stress level though they are not so sure about the future with one another or that at this point they even want it.
>
> It is soothing for the wife to know that her worries are abated and that there will be more peace at home. In turn, the wife is getting the help she needs from the women in the fellowship. The feelings however, are often mixed, because it is not unusual for a great amount of anger to be expressed and as it is uncovered there is more that is revealed. It all has to come out. There is also fear and insecurity, because people have become accustomed to the past ways of the person and now that person is going to change. However, as time goes on and as the person begins to show progress, it is usual for the family and in particular the spouse to experience a tranquility and peacefulness in her or his relationship. Oftentimes, financial worries are a part of the family trauma.   ✳

Families want to know more about the program and how they can be actively involved. The commitment of the wives is evident in the number of women who come to the women's meetings. This support is very important to the men who are on program. The family starts to realize what the alcoholism really is and the wives get some hope too for their husbands. They start to meet women who are just like them and who went through the same hell that their own husbands have put them through. They begin to feel good about themselves.

CHAPTER 5

Brentwood's Outreach

Some of Brentwood's Strategic Services   The purpose of this chapter is to speak of Brentwood's goals for youth and women and to describe the philosophy, purpose and operation of three basic Brentwood programs: 1) Brentwood's Outreach Program in the schools, 2) the Youth Group and 3) the Women's Group.

Brentwood's Emphasis on Youth

Brentwood is eminently conscious of its need to be open to the challenges of youth and of the importance of being a source of hope in a world vested in rage, turmoil and anguish. Since Fr. Paul's message is of a universal dimension, he is able to awaken within youth a sense of belonging. In the Brentwood community they need not fear being mocked or scorned.

Brentwood is sensitively in touch with the pressing cry of afflicted youth who are desperately urging our society to recognize their pain, their sense of being lost and bewildered in a world which to them is devoid of life, meaning and integrity. Their pressing need cannot continue to be ignored. They have been blind to the need for love. The majority of them never could feel it, mostly because of living in a dysfunctional home with alcoholic and addictive parents who could not identify properly with their needs at the critical developmental stages. Hatterer (1980) maintains that youth have learned addictive solutions from parents who have been negligent and abusive both to themselves and to their children:

> The child learns of addiction directly from family models—the sights, sounds, and smells of parental excess. From the very beginning of life he [or she] is cared for by a parent who smokes, drinks, eats, or works too much or who is drugged or overeroticized. The constant smell of tobacco, the touch of a tense and overworked body, being left hungry and neglected by a parent addicted to alcohol or drugs, all leave deep marks that may be passed from generation to generation.... Later in life the person may adopt a

different addiction, consciously rejecting the behavior of his family but not addictiveness itself. For instance, an addiction-prone child avoids the addiction of parents who gamble, drink, or overuse drugs or sex, but turns to addictive eating or work. (p. 18–19)

Society cannot afford to allow its afflicted youth to waste away and be devoured by a system which overlooks their plight. It cannot continue to deprive them from the richness of their needed growth and development. It is important to make an investment in them today so that they can be the responsible citizens of tomorrow. This is such an urgent task since they will be taking their place as future parents. Brentwood as a community is young at heart and provides many young people with the opportunity to celebrate and to come alive again in a way which was never thought possible before by most of them. They are a youthful generation with no sense of roots, with no solid foundation and with no sense of caring and sharing in their lives. They need to be brought into the mainstream of community where they deeply feel a sense of being loved and needed. It is essential that their minds and hearts be opened again so that they can again develop their fullest potential. It is through the healing experience of Brentwood that they can once again find the goodness within themselves and reach out to the woundedness in their peers—those who seriously need a "helping hand" and a "listening ear." Brentwood rightfully challenges youth and raises their hopes and aspirations to more noble heights. It frees them from the bonds of excess, greed, rebelliousness and disillusionment which pervades their stage of development.

Most youths who come to Brentwood do not do so on their own but are usually referred. They are already set in their ways, they do not trust and they are unable to love or feel loved because they have, for the most part, come from a severely dysfunctional home environment. Brentwood helps them to return to their point of woundedness: that moment in time when they were most hurt, pained or rejected. It is not sufficient that they remain locked in a narrow perception of the present but they need to allow the pain of the past to surface so they can utilize their repressed energy as a source of forgiveness of self and of others. They are thus provided the chance to reclaim their past, to enter into it and to move from there to a more fruitful resolution of their present condition. By dealing effectively with the past they can live more peacefully in the present and they can entertain dealing with the future with more strength and certitude. They can now bridge the gap between past and future by living responsibly in the present and by savouring the love and respect they are receiving from their peers on program as well as from the Brentwood staff and the alumni who freely give of their time and energy and act as powerful role models. The youth are helped to resolve conflicts within themselves and to discontinue waging such needless wars. Instead, they are challenged to battle the more pressing issues which deprive them of their zest and dynamism in the "now" of their everyday lives. They can come to grips with their foolish, childish pursuits and entertain a more productive, childlike existence. Matthew Fox points out the difference between these terms:

> ✳ Do not confuse *child-like* and *childish*. Be childlike—as I am, but not childish which is indeed something to outgrow. The childish person has no roots, no sense of the past, no respect for the future and one's responsibility to birth it. Living in the "now" does not mean you remain ignorant of the past or oblivious of the future— it means you bring past and future, old and young, together in you. Now. (p. 198) ✳

It is within the context of a loving and therapeutic community that youth are able to grasp the principles of Brentwood and apply them vigorously in their own lives. It is this tremendous reinforcement which gives them the courage to make a commitment to live in the present and to maximize their creativity and love for life and for other people. By surrendering their false hopes and spurious pursuits they can develop a peace and balance in their lives which is both adventurous and surprisingly rewarding. Brentwood provides youth the opportunity of tapping themselves into a new fruitful and energizing life-line with no substantial sense of loss. It is only fitting that the fruits of Brentwood be poured on the youth who can gain so much from the wealth of its knowledge and experience. It holds the key with which they can unlock the ravaged woundedness of their youth and resurrect their lost identity. Moreover, Brentwood's potential goes beyond its ability to help youth because it is a seminal ground providing youthful leadership—young men and women who are enthusiastically able to extend its spiritual message to countless other youths who still have not come to grips with the more pressing and unresolved problems in their lives. They too can bridge the gap between apathy and celebration, boredom and excitement, cynicism and confidence, despair and hope, indifference and commitment, disengagement and involvement, closedness and openness, pessimism and optimism, violence and gentleness, and trivia and significance.

Brentwood thus provides a valuable service to youth because it has the philosophy, the resources and the means by which to reach them. It is also achieving some relative success in dealing with youth and in healing their woundedness. Unfortunately, the present youth program, as active and flourishing as it is, does not provide for residency. Fr. Paul speaks about the plans for the future:

> ✳ It has been our intention in the last couple of years to focus our attention as a major priority on the program for youths between the ages of thirteen to seventeen. Brentwood has a qualified social worker assigned to this particular responsibility and the board has taken financial responsibility to erect a structure and facility within the next two to three years to house seventy-five to

one hundred in this age group. This is a tremendous undertaking which everyone at Brentwood is committed to and is prepared to carry through.   ✳

Brentwood's Outreach Program in the Schools

Quality of Life

The quality or lack of quality in the life of a community is often exhibited poignantly in the characteristic features of our youth. This can be demonstrated most notably in students as they conduct themselves in the schools. Teachers can, more often than not, be in a position to depict social and psychological issues which require careful intervention. Teachers are conscientious about their educational role but they also realize that they are limited in their ability to reach students who exhibit serious life-pressing problems.

The Brentwood outreach in the schools has been in effect for a number of years but came most strikingly to the fore when an invitation was made from a local high school which had expressed a serious concern about their students in areas related to suicide, alcoholism and countless other problems. The school staff had conducted a survey where they had become increasingly alarmed at the number of attempted suicides in the school, teen pregnancies and the ravaging effects of dysfunctional families. They were able to identify and acknowledge problem areas which they felt Brentwood could address and consequently asked for outside assistance. In effect, Brentwood was summoned because the school was faced with critical life and death issues. The school was at wits' end in terms of a solution and they simply reached out to Brentwood for help. As a result, the Brentwood outreach program was set up in such a way that it would not simply be a "one-time effort" but that it would be, more importantly, an ongoing experience which the school could perpetuate with its own inner resources.

In the Spring of 1985 the Brentwood Program started in the Essex County Separate School Board after a request was made by school board officials. Seven schools were initially involved and by 1987 a total of 15 schools were taking part (*The Brentwood News*, 1989).

Topics Emphasized in the Schools

The Brentwood Program, through the staff, alumni and residents covers topics such as friendship, sharing, appreciation, fears and insecurities, respect and peer pressure. Students, during their adolescence (the process of transition from childhood to maturity) have many pressures placed on them to conform to peer group standards. The Brentwood Program instills in students the importance of being able to share with others the problems they are experiencing (*The Brentwood News*, 1989).

It is important that the major themes covered be personally relevant to the students involved. This is sometimes relatively easy to do since most people, referring to the Brentwood talks, exclaim: "It seems that the people are speaking directly to me and that they know the details of my own life. I feel that I am being understood in my own life circumstances. It seems that I have never felt like this before." Topics are assigned sensitively by Brentwood staff according to the needs of the students as the program progresses. Examples of topics include such areas as:

FRIENDSHIP — The importance of having a true friend that one can talk to about problems as well as good times.
Respect in friendship; honesty.
Appreciation of friends.

SHARING — The importance of sharing what goes on in one's life and how one feels about it.
Not trying to go through life alone.

APPRECIATION — Who and what one appreciates in one's life today.

FEARS AND INSECURITIES — Feelings of inferiority.
Fear of failure, rejection, or of being laughed at.
Anger caused by fear.
Fear of social events (dances, family celebrations, holidays, i.e., times associated with drinking, tension, etc.).

PEER PRESSURE — Fear of "not fitting in."
The need to conform.
The difficulty of making choices of what to conform to.
Dating, forming close relationships, drinking and drugs.

RESPECT — Of self.
Of others.

CELEBRATION — Opportunity for team members, students and teachers to share positive outcomes of the program.

The Brentwood Philosophy in the Schools

Fr. Paul's approach to developing programs for youth has been basically to "nip in the bud" some critical social issues occurring in the lives of teenage students which otherwise would not be brought to the fore until much later when the damage is sometimes irreparable. This preventive type of intervention can assist the younger generation to avoid the trap of "learned helplessness" stemming from dysfunctional family binds and a pervasive sense of aloneness and alienation.

The central goal of the Brentwood Program in the schools is to implant in students belief in the importance of sharing with at least one trusted adult when there are problems and not to try to go through the turmoil alone. Respect for the individual and confidentiality in groups and one-on-ones is continually stressed. The very heart of the Brentwood outreach program flows from a simple principle: "People, and particularly children, need other people in their lives with whom they can relate in a meaningful way." In Brentwood terminology, this is referred to as *caring* and *sharing*. The Brentwood experience teaches students their need for people in their lives whom they can trust in their own growth and with whom they can confide the "ups and downs" of their own journey, with all the pain, the joy and confusion which it entails. Young people need such trustworthy people with whom they can be truly honest. It is believed that this type of supportive encounter prevents the young from slipping into negativity and a defeatist "poor me" attitude, which diminishes self-worth and eventually renders their lives useless.

Brentwood's outreach program can be seen as analogous to teaching young children to read and write at a very early age. If one can teach young people the devastation of alcohol, drug and substance abuse at an early age, it then becomes possible to instill in them the value and importance of life being fully lived in the present. They can thus be prepared for living life in the real world. As one alumna recalls, by knowing the warning signs they can be more equipped to deal with them (emphases by the responder):

※   I remember what the signs were for me in my childhood. In my case it was a matter of defiance and deception. I was *closed, impatient, defiant, hostile* and *destructive* with my family and I was not able to be "part of." I was *argumentative, vindictive, destructive* and *rebellious* at home. My resistance, my lying, and my inability to listen simply escalated. I thought my parents were against me and I projected my anger and disappointment on to them. I was simply convinced that I had to exclude myself and do things my way. Every time I asked for something and they said; "No" I interpreted this as their not understanding me or their not loving me. I did not realize that the "no" was for my own good.

At school, I was *very closed, self-centred, disengaged, introverted* and *confused*. I was *full of fear* and wanted so much to be "part of" but I did not know how to go about it. I was always wishing, hoping and *daydreaming*. I wanted to get away from my family. I wanted to *escape*. I was always *depressed* and *angry* while not knowing why. I had a strong and inordinate self-will. I *shut out people* and completely *lost interest in life*.

I had *no balance* in my life. I could never experience any happy medium. I had terrible *mood swings* and I increasingly wanted to be *alone*. Even with my "aloneness," I was unable to be "at home" with myself let alone comfortable with others. I spent so much of my waking hours turned painfully into myself. I was notorious for engaging in self-pity and bouts of depression. I ended up with *no self-confidence* and no sense of humor. Nothing in life was any longer pleasant or enjoyable.

I always saw myself as a *loner*, and that I was different from others ever since I can remember. My life was seclusive and insular. I always wondered why others played sports while I always sat on a bench with a note from the doctor *excusing* me from sports. Steeped in *self-pity*, I asked myself: "Why can't I play sports"? I felt *isolated* at a very early age. My school mates were on one side enjoying themselves and I was over on the other *disheartened, fearful, dejected, miserable* and *forlorn*. I had all the warning signs but I didn't know it at the time. ✳

The Brentwood model, however, is more than a merely intellectual teaching tool. Providing information alone to youth will not do it. It encompasses much more broadly the true meaning of education or *educere* which means to "draw forth." The sharing which is done by alumni and senior people on program actually draws from the students cognitive, emotional and behavioural responses concerning the devastating effects of alcoholism, addiction and drug abuse. Students are thus able to effectively get in touch with their hurt and pain and their diminished lack of self-worth. They are provided with a real-life picture. Seeing that others like themselves and of their own age have been able courageously to make a breakthrough in their lives, gives them hope that there is help available and that all is not lost. Students will actually say: "*Their* story is *my* story. Their past is so similar to my own. I want to have what they have."

Brentwood's outreach program in the schools is a systematic effort of reaching students who are at a very formative and impressionable crossroad in their lives. It provides for exposure to "real-life" experiences of people whose lives have been crushed by the effects of alcohol, drugs and addiction. Students are confronted with people whose lives have been turned around for the better because of their present ability to relate to others and to exercise their fullest potential. It is this very exposure which has a "ripple" effect on students and which invites them to channel their energy towards improving the quality of their own lives as it relates to their home, school and social life.

The Brentwood Experience in the Schools

To cite one specific example, Brentwood conducted one of its outreach programs in a local high school. The time-frame included sixteen on-site visits consisting of thirty-two teams of mostly six to seven with no fewer than four to five members. Two teams each comprising sixteen groups, would alternate each week for a period of sixteen weeks. Each session was for a thirty-minute period. A general presentation was made and then the group was broken down into yet smaller sections for more personal discussion. The small groups provided an opportunity for students to ask more pressing and detailed questions of a personal nature. Though the formal sessions were for thirty minutes, it was agreed by the school that more time would be provided for those students who wanted to stay longer and have a one-on-one with one of the Brentwood presenters. As stated in the guideline:

> Quite often, a student wishes to speak to a team member on an individual basis about a personal problem. These "one-on-ones" are encouraged since they often serve to clear up a "little" problem before it becomes a "big" problem. Students can ask for one-on-ones following the group sharing session and allowance is made for this because of its importance.

Any problems of a significant nature were brought back to the attention of the appropriate guidance staff. In one example, a student was fearful of going home because his father was always drunk and abusive. The student was encouraged to bring this matter to the attention of his guidance counsellor. It was further understood that the Brentwood outreach was there as an opportunity for sharing and for being of help where possible. The presenters made sure that they would not infringe on the private space of the students but were reminded that they were going into the schools as guests and that they were not there to "grandstand" and thus defeat the simple message which was to be given.

The Brentwood outreach in the schools is actually a carry-over of what goes on at Brentwood on a daily basis. It can be seen in the image of a "mobile unit" wherein the resources of team members, made up of the staff, the alumni and the residents, are brought to bear on the lives of students. The commanding influence, which is created within the school, is due to the honest and down-to-earth one-on-one sharing by the team members. These are people who have a basic sense of the Brentwood spirit. They share (1) *the past,* how their lives were in shambles before Brentwood, (2) *the present,* the insights they are gaining from their exposure to the Brentwood philosophy and the manner in which they are learning to turn their lives around in a more mature and responsible fashion and (3) *the future,* their hopes and aspirations for a richer and more quality-filled life. They acknowledge the damage they have caused others and how they have had to ask for forgiveness. It is the very sincerity of their sharing which touches the heart of the students and which produces a "ripple effect" causing them to carefully examine more honestly and realistically the quality of their own lives. The impact of the presenters is seen not only in the tears of specific individual students but in the intensity of their sharing which occurs in the small groups as well as in one-on-one sessions which follow the formal time together.

For the first time in their lives the young presenters share with their own schoolmates about the incessant "hell" they were living in at home because they had a dramatic fear of allowing anyone to know the disturbing truth of their existence. They were terrorized within themselves before their recovery process but are now able to "let go" and release the tremendous pressure that had built up within them.

Although teenagers can be rather disengaged, in any formal presentation, it is not the attitude and atmosphere which prevails during the Brentwood presentations. On the contrary, the response was one of interest evidenced by the quality of their questions in the small groups where they were able to internalize the message.

Since a considerable number of the team members are themselves teenagers, this makes a marvelous impression on students who can receive the message more openly and meaningfully because it is sincere and comes from "one of their own age," much like peer-teaching. The peer members share their lives at a much deeper level than the surface elements of alcohol, drugs or addiction. They reveal the more devastating spiritual bankruptcy which occurred to them as a result of their blindness and their inability to love. They divulge about the deeper issues that lurked within them and which they have bottled up for many years. Some students are actually dumb-founded that they are so candid about their lives, especially when it is a person of their own age level, and this seems to have a much more powerful impact on their lives. The greatest expert in the world might come and talk and not necessarily have the same impact as "one of their own." Further, the ripple effect on both teachers and students creates a bond of mutual respect and sharing which is carried on in the day-to-day activities of the school.

The team members are themselves also profoundly touched by their experience in the schools, through the candid response of the students. As one presenter exclaims:

> ∗ I feel a real "high". It seems that I get more out of it than they do. By a strange twist of fate, the more I share my story the more deeply I am touched by the sincerity and good-will of others. It is like happiness, if you give it away, it seems to come right back to you. What I give to others in a positive vein is returned to me one hundredfold. ∗

The written evaluations from the schools provided by the individual students rated the Brentwood presentations very highly. As one staff member relates: "If one were to put in dollars and cents the immense value of the effectiveness of the Brentwood program in the schools, it would be virtually impossible to put a specific dollar sign on it because of its immeasurable worth and significance."

The good that comes out of Brentwood's outreach to the schools is found in the testimony of both teachers and students. All the letters of thanks and appreciation which have been received at Brentwood have expressed a gratitude for the lasting impression which the Brentwood extension program made in the schools with its honesty and forthrightness. As one respondent poignantly comments:

✳   There are no facades presented. Each speaks from the very pain of their journey. This type of testimony touches me deeply and calls me to reflect on my own life. I was awed by how they described their lives in the past in contrast to the more dynamic transformation which they are experiencing today.   ✳

As a result of the Brentwood outreach and because of the lasting "ripple-effect," some students have eventually come to Brentwood in the full-time program. As one student reflects on his experience of the presenters and the impact of his own decision to get help for himself:

✳   Those who shared with us were down-to-earth, ordinary people very much like myself. I came to see the devastation in my own life, the destructive path I was choosing and I suddenly realized that I wanted a "piece" of the good life that they were experiencing. I knew I needed help and I was reasonably confident that if Brentwood could work for them then it could most likely work for me. It was for this reason and because of the overwhelming pain and confusion in my own life that I chose to be admitted into Brentwood and to go through the ninety-day program. As I look back it has made all the difference in the world. Now I can be there for others who still hurt the way I did because today I have a heart for other people.

I realize now ever so clearly, following my experience at Brentwood, that I am never alone as long as I am able to care and share with others. I can now be strong for those who are on a "dead end road" because of their inability to share and confide. I can be there for them in a way I never dreamt was possible. I never have to be alone again and neither do they. If I can give them a taste of the "good life" now, it will prevent them from having to go through the needless pain and torturous hell which I experienced. Just as Brentwood has left an indelible mark on me, I feel confidant that I can leave a positive impact on some of my peers who are still suffering unnecessarily.   ✳

In addition to the service which Brentwood provides to the schools, it has been asked to assist with the Christian Brothers' annual retreats for high school students where seniors on program share their stories with the retreatants. This outreach furnishes an opportunity to "plant a seed" and provides youth an opportunity to hear, listen and respond to the truth within themselves. They are given a chance to get in touch with their feelings and to cut through the blindness within themselves. Often this self-awareness motivates the youth to seek help.

The Youth Group   The "Number One" problem confronting youth
————————————————   today is the pervasive presence of drugs in our society. As mentioned previously, the Brentwood philosophy holds that

neither drug nor alcohol abuse can be understood as a problem of substance abuse alone, since there is a deeper underlying condition—a sickness—that must be healed. Usually this sickness originates in the family and must be dealt with in the family. It is not only the presence of drugs but the detrimental impact which alcoholism, addiction and substance abuse has upon the family members. There is a spiritual illness, in fact, in our whole culture in which the family exists, and which is a seed-bed for not only addictions, but even satanic cults. As Bishop Sherlock exclaims:

> ✳   One of the more important elements about Brentwood is its emphasis on youth. I am absolutely convinced of the authenticity of Fr. Paul's presentation of the Gospel as something of great consequence. It has more important ramifications because of the tremendous impetus for *young people* who today tend to be living solely for themselves. Nearly everything in our culture leads to self indulgence. Consequently, young people are particularly vulnerable to addiction of one sort or another through drugs and alcohol, because they are searching for *meaning*. A life that is purely self-indulgent has no meaning.
>
> The suicidal issue is one of major concern in our society today. A recent program called "Vision" dealt with the issue of Satanism in young people and how some of the heavy metal rock groups are putting out lyrics which recommend killing others and self-suicide. Satanic cults suggest that by killing the self, a person will emerge into a reincarnation of a better life. It is a total perversion of the Gospel. It destroys hope in life and is life-denying. Yet it is very common out there in the everyday world. This program "Vision" was indeed terrifying because it portrayed the extent to which such issues are embedded into the fabric of our society. In his daily talks, Fr. Paul strikes at the very core of this dark and sinister culture identifying it with the destructive forces of alcoholism and self-will. Laying the axe to the root of this villainous tree, his message is entirely *life-affirming*.   ✳

In 1981, there were several alumnae who approached Fr. Paul with the possibility of providing some type of program or activity for the youth. The youth group began its operation out of St. Hubert's school in South Windsor. There was a perceived need for this type of service for youth. It started with thirty young people both male and female and today it has escalated to over 160.

What Youth does Brentwood Serve?
The Brentwood Youth Group is devoted to helping youth from ages 8–18 who have been disturbed by the ravaging disease of alcoholism. In most instances one or both parents are alcoholic and they have

been through the Brentwood program or are now undergoing treatment. Most of the youth in this program are considered to be *non-alcoholic.*

The Philosophy
The purpose of the youth program is basically the same as that of the overall Brentwood philosophy: to provide a warm nurturing environment where young people can come and make friends and be effectively engaged in relationship-building. At an early age, most of these youth are not capable of getting involved in group sharing at any deep level. In fact the early age group, of eight to nine years, is kept fairly casual and entertaining, since the main point at this stage is to gain trust and confidence.

Goals of the Youth Group
The Brentwood Youth Group began in 1981 and is under the direction of Fr. Paul and a team of qualified leaders. Its four main goals consist of:

1.   Providing understanding and healing to those children who have been adversely affected by the disease;

2.   Providing youth with practice in the fundamental life skills they need to continue the healing process; i.e., the ability to talk about deep feelings, and a better knowledge of their own strengths and weaknesses. This sharing and growth occurs within the context of a supporting environment consisting of other children their own age and adult leaders.

3.   Heightening consciousness concerning the impact of drugs as well as informing and educating the broader community about the resources in the local area which deal with these problems.

4.   Providing healing and renewal to counteract the generational consequence of alcoholism, addiction and substance abuse.

The Youth Group Steering Committee
There is a Steering Committee made up of nine group leaders who have been involved with the youth group for at least a year or longer. This committee meets every two months to discuss upcoming topics and events. They examine problems and consider solutions while working closely with Fr. Paul in the decision-making process. The Youth Leaders meet briefly before each weekly session to carry out whichever topic has been planned and discussed for the specific evening. The activities are geared toward the particular topic chosen. Different leaders are assigned responsibility for the eight-to-ten-year-old group, and others are assigned for the junior and senior group.

The Actual Program
The Youth Group regularly meets on Tuesday evenings, and is made up of four individual groups—the 8- to 10-year-olds, the junior

group, 11–13, the senior group 14–16 and the young adult group 17–21. A presentation is made to each group by one of the group members from the steering committee. Audio-visual materials are often used and at times an up-to-date song or a film which is of particular significance is used. On occasion, speakers are invited to address the youth.

Following the main assembly, the youth are broken into smaller groups and asked to focus their sharing and discussion on the specific presentation. They are also asked to relate the various themes to the important events in their own lives or to the issues which may be problematic to them. On some occasions, the leaders will have a list of questions and will invite each participant to give their response to the various questions.

The youth are invited to become specific as to the role they have played in the various scenarios they bring up for discussion and how it relates to the Brentwood principles. These sessions are from 6:30 p.m. to 7:30 p.m. The remaining hour is for recreation and planned activity. Other activities involve roller skating, dancing, an annual picnic and selective weekend retreats.

One-on-ones are always encouraged, particularly at the senior and junior levels, and occasionally in the eight-to-tens. By engendering a positive attitude and disposition in each participant, they realize that the youth group is always a significant place for them to come to.

Unlike the seniors, who are eager to share one-to-one, most of the junior group are going through a developmental phase in which they are more or less resistant and hesitant. They are in that awkward position of growth, development and transition and the most difficult to deal with considering the aspect of their lives which they are going through. As to the seniors, the Minnesota Multiphasic Personality Inventory (MMPI) test is administered for some, particularly those who are more troubled. This provides the opportunity to obtain a better picture of their psycho-social status and to offer a more suitable treatment.

Young people are never coerced to come to the youth group but are encouraged to do so. According to the staff, the vast majority of them are coming because they are motivated and genuinely interested in what happens: they want to be at Brentwood and are reaping its benefits.

The Monday Evening Youth Group

The Monday evening group includes youth, 8–13, who are exhibiting problems in the regular Tuesday evening group. They have been unable to sit attentively or participate adequately and cause difficulty for the other members as well as the group leaders because of their defiance and lack of cooperation. Members are reassigned to the Tuesday group when they show improvement in their performance.

The purpose of the Monday evening sessions is to help build a trust within the group by means of specific activities which will draw out the more positive dimensions of their personality and their relating to the real world. Members of this group require support and understanding but they also need a structure where discipline plays an important role for them. Some may be experiencing dysfunctional problems at home, as well as continued pain and isolation, or they may be having serious difficulties at school or in their social lives. The rules and regulations have to be clear, concrete and specific for them and they need to know what the limits are. They need to realize how to respect authority and to behave within a clearly defined social context. There is a need for balance between being too strict on one hand and being too lenient on the other.

The Young Adult Group

As members of the younger group reach the age of seventeen, they move to the senior level, where the sharing becomes more profound. By this time some have established friendships and are able to actually come into the day program and become immersed in the recovery process. This is particularly true for those who have been heavily involved in drugs and alcohol.

In the ideal situation, the senior youth and the young adults are able to be leaders and role models for the juniors, similar to the way the alumni function in a supportive capacity with the fellowship and with those on program. This modelling process within the youth group is one which is continually refined so as to provide the most meaningful type of concentration and expansion.

One method of approaching the younger people is through the use of puppeteers. Seniors create their own puppets as an expression of themselves and as a channel to work with the younger population. The puppets are personal, life-size, a marionette type imbued with a great deal of character and personality. Such activity provides a tremendous impetus for the younger group and at the same time provides an avenue for instilling self-confidence and self-esteem in the seniors since it is an experience which is so dramatically individual and creative. It draws them out of themselves and is a vehicle which enhances self-disclosure.

A Full-Time Youth Coordinator

A full-time youth coordinator was appointed in the winter of 1990 to carry out the aims and objectives of the youth program in a more concerted and unified manner. It was felt that such an appointment would provide a more unified approach.

Areas Requiring Special Consideration

One area which remains very sensitive is that of sexual self-disclosure. Not only is this a taboo area for most but it is a very delicate area for both those who have been sexually abused and for others who have been the perpetrators. In order to do the necessary screening for these issues to be brought to the surface, Brentwood provides testing and treatment programs. These are especially necessary because some teenagers have hidden this aspect for so very long that it has negatively pervaded all dimensions of their lives. Those who are victims of sexual abuse or those who have done the victimizing are involved in one way or another with Fr. Paul, the youth program coordinator and the resident psychologist.

Role of the Youth Group Leaders

All Brentwood youth leaders at the present time are volunteers. Most are alumni or wives of alumnae who have gone through the program. There are some who have had a son or daughter come through Brentwood. Volunteers are expected to make a six-month commitment. Most are there because they care and are genuinely interested in working with the young people. Matters pertaining to sexual assault or physical abuse are brought to the attention of the program coordinator so that it can be channeled to the proper professional staff.

The group leaders provide a positive parental image for these youth which combines warmth and gentleness with security and direction and it is expected that the young people, in turn will respond and grow. It is important for them to learn that the leaders will not allow them to hurt either themselves or others, or become irresponsible. The leaders must communicate to them the nurturance, warmth and respect which many of them have not previously experienced, thus fulfilling a surrogate parental role.

Working with youth, at times, can be very draining and exhausting because of the tremendous energy the children have and because of the numerous demands they can place upon the leaders. There are the normal issues involved in the growing pains of any program as well as the fact that the teenagers are growing through enormous changes within themselves.

Parents were involved at one time in the youth program but this was discontinued for a number of reasons. They would meet separately with staff to discuss various concerns about raising their children while the youth group was being conducted in another area. They were also involved to some extent in the sports activities but it was discovered that all such involvement was becoming problematic so it was discontinued. Instead, a parent night informs the parents of the progress which is being made in the youth group.

The Future

The youth group is still in its infancy in terms of having structures and facilities consistent with the Brentwood philosophy. With the new facilities which are planned, the youth will have the opportunity to come to Brentwood every day much like the alumni do and an "open night" will be provided which will span the entire week and provide opportunities for youth to meet and to share. For the time being, Brentwood is offering a viable program until the resources are in place to provide for a larger and more comprehensive program with the appropriate facilities. Future plans will provide proper sports facilities like a baseball diamond, a volleyball court and rooms for counselling and individualized and group sessions. The enhanced physical facility will allow for more volunteers to provide their time and energy with the youth program.

The Women's Group — The women's meeting is an essential aspect of the services which Brentwood provides. Since Brentwood recognizes the disease of alcoholism as a family disease, it feels obligated to have a program for the whole family. It is for this reason that there are programs for spouses, the mothers, and fiancees as well as a program for youth. At least ninety percent of the women who have a married spouse or a common-law spouse and who come into Brentwood have been exposed for the majority of their lives to persistent negativity and ravaged emotionally by the fatal effects of the disease. They simply gravitated to their present relationship. They most likely grew up in an alcoholic environment where feelings and emotions were severely suppressed. Their very attraction to an alcoholic personality indicates that this would be the type of person to whom they would have a strong attraction. Most of these women have been ravaged emotionally by the negative effects of the disease. In fact, the experience of Brentwood is that some of these women end up in worse shape emotionally and psychologically than their spouses who are on program.

History of the Women's Meetings

Brentwood has provided weekly women's meetings for the last seven years. Previous to this, these as well as the couples' meetings, were only held once per month. Next, when Brentwood began to use St. Hubert's school, the women's meetings were held weekly and for the past six years, since the present property was procured, they have been held three times per week. Approximately two hundred and ten to two hundred and twenty women attend these meetings each week.

In addition to this, there are Brentwood groups which meet weekly in London, Oakville, Chatham, Wallaceburg, Sudbury and Detroit. These groups originated with the men alumnae and grew with the addition of the wives. If a man from London, for example, comes on program, the Brentwood staff contacts the local group in that area concerning the wife, the mother or the fiancee, whatever the case might be. In turn, the women in these groups contact the spouses who then attend the groups which are both for men and for women.

The Content, Structure and Process of the Meetings

A team of women leaders is chosen and rotates every six months. A woman from the team is responsible for organizing the logistics: getting names and phone numbers of newcomers, making announcements, sitting people down before the meetings and making sure that the newcomers are warmly received and welcomed. Another team of women who have been coming to Brentwood for at least a year act as the leaders for the various small groups which follow the larger meeting.

What occurs in the women's meetings is similar to what transpires in the regular meetings. Both the talk and the discussion which follow centre around the same major topic for that week which is being presented to those on full program. Thus there is a systematic parallel between what the husbands, sons or fiances are receiving on program and what the women are getting at the women's meetings and this parallel process provides a mutual flow of communication between the wives, mothers or fiancees on one hand and those on program because they are being exposed and touched by the same topic.

The actual talks at the women's meetings last twenty to thirty minutes and usually include sharing from two or three women who have been actively involved with Brentwood for some time. On some rare occasions when staff are not available, women themselves conduct the meetings. These are led by women who have the spirit, the knowledge and the discipline necessary to conduct the group adequately.

The Importance of Phone Contacts

Since the women meet only once a week, the importance of making regular daily phone calls to other women is strongly emphasized. It is imperative that they develop the courage and take the risk to ask for the phone numbers of at least five or six women who have been coming to Brentwood over an extended period of time. It provides an opportunity for them to get in touch with people who are genuinely "winners" as opposed to "losers," all the while building up their self-esteem and their self-confidence.

For women who are wives and mothers, the phone contacts allow them to be in touch with other people without feeling the guilt of leaving their family obligations or of not being there for the children. The phone contact allows them to be relaxed without worrying excessively that a clock is ticking to warn them that they should be at home. Since many of them feel that they have damaged their children in one way or another, they do not want to feel that they are in any way deserting them now when they are in the process of recovery. As one lady remarked: "Nothing can compare to the wonderful feeling you get when you have just had a meaningful phone call and in closing the other lady says: 'You don't know how much your listening and sharing has helped me'."

Meeting the Needs of the New Women

For the new women, Brentwood has provided an additional session following the women's meetings. These meetings provide an opportunity for new women to share their concerns and to raise any particular questions they might have. It also gives the counselling staff a chance to get to know the women whose husbands are on program and to learn about their marriage and their family situation. As the women become more comfortable with the staff, they begin to share at a deeper level of self-disclosure and they are more willing to consult and seek direction.

When women are counselled on a regular basis, they are often encouraged and directed to write *inventories*. Written inventory is undertaken after the women have done a sufficient amount of sharing with the other women and when they are ready to share more openly at a deeper level. They are asked to do this in two specific phases. In the *first phase* they are invited to cover, as far back as they can recall in their life span on a feeling level, all the hurts that they have received in their lives. In the *second phase*, they are then asked to write all the hurts they themselves have caused other people whether knowingly or unknowingly. As one woman mentions:

> ✳ Inventory has given me some great *breakthroughs*, particularly when I was dealing with some deep-seated problems. My submissions help the staff who read them to discover unresolved issues to which I am blind. Through their insight and direction, I am given a freedom to see things in a new light—in a way I would not have been able to see by myself. ✳

Progression into the Full-Time Program
A clearer picture is provided as to how much help a good number of these women need when one looks at the percentage of women who have eventually enrolled in the full ninety-day program. Recently, within a three-month period, there were forty-six women who graduated from the full-time program and twenty-seven of these were from the women's program. They came to realize that they needed more constant and intense help which is more readily provided in the regular program.

Fr. Paul is somewhat reluctant to accept these women on the full-time program if they do not have the alcohol or substance abuse problem nor will he accept them into the program unless they have been attending the women's meeting for a year or more. It is felt that seventy-five percent of those who come to the women's meetings would "dearly love" to have three months of full program but the reality is that they do not all need it. For this reason, discretion has to be used in determining who actually needs the full ninety-day program.

The Reward of Working with the Women's Group
It is very rewarding work for the particular staff involved with the women's group and with the individual cases that are presented daily. It is felt that it takes a great deal of courage and determination for the vast majority of these women to actually set foot on the Brentwood property and to continue coming on a regular basis. At least fifty percent show almost immediately how readily they grasp the positive elements of the program. This seems to be so since they are so spiritually "hungry" for a resource of this nature. After seven years in the making, there are still a sufficient number of women who continue coming regularly to the various meetings and there are a large number of women alumni who have established a solidity about themselves and who act as *leaven*. It does not take very long to witness how a new

woman in her initial encounter with Brentwood begins to move ahead almost instantly in self-worth, self-dignity and self-respect.

These women are not only learning about their husband's sickness and recovery process, they are also becoming aware of their own. One of the happiest statements that can be heard is when a woman openly acknowledges: "I am in recovery too." She recognizes and accepts her own issues and now can act constructively on her new insights. The women are distracted from a negative home environment to a powerful and rewarding Brentwood fellowship. In addition to the joy and gratification the staff receive, the women also take great delight in their investment in the women's meetings. As one lady mentions:

> ✻   For me it is the warmth you feel when through your sharing you lighten another person's burden. It is consoling to come in contact with so many people who are like myself. The reward for many of us is simply in seeing a smile where just a short while ago there was a devastating pain. It is priceless to see the inner beauty of another person and for her to be able to acknowledge her own inner beauty. It is most rewarding.   ✻

Future Plans

It is Fr. Paul's wish to eventually have larger facilities where the women will be able to come to Brentwood at any time of the day or evening. The same applies with the children and the youth.

CHAPTER **6**

Charity House and Brentwood's Beginnings

In the Beginning...

Fr. Paul has fond memories of his beginning work in the field of alcoholism. His interest in working with alcoholics all started around the year 1952 when he was involved in the Air Force. A number of the wives who were overburdened and in desperation came to him for advice and direction about their alcoholic husbands. Fr. Paul held the first AA meeting on an Air Force Base in Canada. As he recalls:

> ✳   I never had any difficulty to "fit in" when it came to people or to be there for people or with people whether they were from "the street" or whether they were from the professions. My life was always geared and centered around people. I was never embarrassed or threatened by people. I found it just as easy to work with the people at Charity House as I did with the students in the schools or the people in the parish no matter what their background was or their financial status. I could easily bounce from the hospitals to the schools, to the rectory, to the church, to their homes; there was no conflict, since to me they were all one and the same.   ✳

At first, Fr. Paul did not do any counselling himself other than perhaps offer help and direction to the wives. For the most part he stayed back and listened. Anyone acquainted with Fr. Paul would realize that this would be quite a feat for him not to immediately roll up his sleeves and dive right into it. On the contrary, he permitted himself to be led by the recovering alcoholic who, in turn, would heal the wounded alcoholic. The majority of time he would get another alcoholic to talk to the person who was afflicted with the disease. For example, if a person came to him for help he would automatically call another alcoholic. This is how he used the original seven men with the alcoholics in the parish. It took about five or six years before he moved beyond merely sitting down and listening, not doing anything himself and simply letting the two alcoholics be there for each other. He got out of the way and allowed one alcoholic to heal the other alcoholic until he developed the knack of it himself and the confidence to intervene in their lives. In time, he was able to minister to them in his own unique way.

After twenty-five years he has earned the right to directly intervene in the lives of those afflicted with alcoholism and with those who are addicted in one way or another. Now, he actually has a responsibility to intervene because he has the "practice wisdom" which comes with both time, patience, compassion and experience.

Justifying a Recovery Home in the City of Windsor

A preparatory stage to Fr. Paul's lifelong involvement in the field of alcoholism started when he regularly met in his rectory with seven men who were alcoholic and belonged to AA. There is a debt of gratitude extended to these seven men: Bill C., Eddie C., Roy D., Steve B., Al H., Wilf G. and Ray B. Fr. Paul felt that the group had to extend itself and reach out to other people. It was this insight to expand that provided him with the impetus for creating Charity House.

The group met for a year or two and he told them that if they were to continue to meet they would have to go out into the community and bring more people into their group and do something for those who were alcoholic and in need.

In 1965, there was very little being done by the government for people who had disabilities, especially the men in the city. Often they were without funds since there weren't as many social services provided for them as completely as they are offered today. As a result, many of them had neither a place to sleep nor anything to eat except what they received downtown. According to Kay Ryan:

> ✳   Basically, there was nothing being done for them regarding their problems with alcoholism. Some of them would drift into AA meetings but most of the time it was merely for companionship, a place to stay and a chance for a cup of coffee or a doughnut. AA was not sufficient for them to make the breakthrough with their alcoholism.   ✳

Fr. Paul was aware of a number of men who had no means of income and who had nowhere to live. Many of them were sleeping under the Peabody bridge, in old cars or in doorways. At that time the welfare system was inadequate for these single men and it was then that Fr. Paul decided that something should be done about these people who were mostly alcoholic. Though they did not necessarily want help for their alcoholic problem, they nonetheless, needed food and a place to sleep. Consequently, Fr. Paul attended to their basic needs at a time when they had nothing.

The issues of alcoholism in the local area were further complicated in some instances by industry, the economy, family, social conditions and the turmoil within the church itself. All of these elements fitted together because at that time (1965) the economy was in a recession, some companies were moving out of Windsor, and others were laying off workers. It seemed at the time that there were more people on the street than at other times.

Obstacles Encountered in Opening Charity House

Charity House began in a restaurant on Wyandotte Street East but was left on its own with only a few friends and supporters in the beginning. When the news got out that Fr. Paul was trying to buy the Independent Order of Foresters (I.O.O.F.) hall at 634 Chilver Road, residents and business people in the area, about one hundred and twenty-five, took up a petition to prevent him. They were afraid it would undermine the value of their own homes and businesses. Moreover, the residential people feared that their children would be endangered by the type of person who would frequent such a facility.

Undaunted by this opposition, Fr. Paul, as usual, forged ahead with vigor and enthusiasm. His fervor and excitement was contagious. Without knowing it, he had a certain charisma and magnetism which attracted people, and within a short period of time managed to engender a tremendous amount of unity and cooperation. The residents in the neighborhood soon found that their fears were unfounded, and ironically a number of them and their children ended up helping to serve meals at Charity House. In Fr. Paul's own words:

> ✳ Every time an individual attempts to do something, society or the community is sort of a watchdog to check out whether such people are simply "do-gooders," or whether they are "fly-by-night" people. This is a good and normal safeguard which is legitimate for the sake of the area and those who are invested in it. If an enterprise is real, one will stick with it and it will thrive. If it is not real, such adventures will simply die or fade away. In the case of Charity House, it was not very long before there was a genuine breakthrough with the community. The usual need of money and cooperation from other agencies were simply normal concerns that would be experienced with almost any new venture. There was nothing out of the ordinary in terms of resistance or contention. ✳

The Historical Trend toward Alcoholism at the Time of Charity House

According to Kay Ryan, AA was the major available service for the alcoholic at Charity House. She recalls:

> ✳ The seven men who worked with Fr. Paul in the beginning were members of AA and went to Fr. Paul weekly for extra counselling. They were actually former business people who had lost

everything and were working their way back. Their marriages had been in jeopardy and in danger of breaking up and they were in real difficulty and turmoil.

At first, Charity House helped many people who were not interested in getting sober. They had nothing and they rather enjoyed their drinking. Charity House did not interfere with that, though it was clear that they were not allowed to drink on the premises or bring bottles into the building. There were experiences where staff actually had to take bottles away from men who were coming into the building. Staff were not afraid to do this because they knew that these men would not retaliate or harm them. They were not allowed to drink in the building though staff knew that they actually did drink when they went out.   ✳

The First Clientele of Charity House

Society has had different names for these alcoholic people such as "rounders," "the man on the street," or the "wino." Most of them were homeless. These men were practically all on welfare when they could get it, or they just depended on each other's friendship where they did a lot of sharing as to where they slept, what they had to eat or what they had to drink. Consequently, at the very beginning, Charity House catered mostly to those who would be considered "down and out" as opposed to those in the upper strata such as professionals who were alcoholic or those referred to as "closet alcoholics" who frequented Charity House. The "off and on" clientele were a suspicious group, most of whom slept outside in any opportune place with a piece of cardboard for a mattress and someone's discarded newspaper for a blanket.

Most of the people in Charity House were the real "down-and-out" who did not have a place to wash or shower or who wore the same clothes day in and day out. Most people at that time had a fixed stereotype of alcoholics as merely those who eat from garbage cans and who sleep anywhere they can. The ones who were encountered at Charity House for the first ten years tended to confirm that stereotype.

The Basic Problems of the Down-and-Out

What was most serious with these types of alcoholics is that they only trusted other down-and-out alcoholics and were suspicious of anyone else. They were very lonely people who had a strong loyalty to one another and had no use for anyone else except when it was to their advantage to "use" them or to "con" them. They were also very depressed people and were very skeptical about anyone who tried to help them out. They would always take from people without any thought of giving anything back in return. And while they had an allegiance to their own, they were most hesitant about trusting anyone at Charity House.

These frequenters of Charity House had the same problems as alcoholics have today. They had problems living with people, and with so many experiences of rejection by their families, other workers or with the welfare system, they ended up isolated and shattered. They were unable to cope, except by means of escaping to the drink. They were very leery when the doors of Charity House opened. When Charity House came into operation in a former restaurant, the volunteers had to go out and bring these people in from the streets, because they were so paranoid and distrustful. They did not believe that there was anything in the community that would be helpful to them. They had stooped so low that they could not trust that anyone would want them without some kind of strings being attached.

Characteristics of the Alcoholic
Specific features that were observed in the very beginning at Charity House were the alcoholic's inability to trust, their strong tendency to "use" or take advantage of people who tried to help them, and their lack of any genuine desire to change. In fact, they had an intense fear of changing their lives. They were so used to living the way they did that they did not feel any need to change. They did not want to give up their friendships with one another with its little cliques or groups who had immense loyalty to each other. Further they felt a certain freedom in that there was no need for them to be accountable to anyone. They therefore always resisted the efforts of social workers to get them to change their lifestyle. Although they were very much set in their ways, they almost had to "take advantage" of Charity House before they could develop trust. On its part Charity House had no grand illusions of what to expect from the alcoholic, considering the reality of their lives, but simply understood where they were coming from and accepted them as they were.

At their core, they were all very good and lovable people who simply needed a helping hand and somebody to understand and to care about them. The staff at Charity House became real friends with these people and close-knit relationships developed. They had gone off track and Charity House provided them with an opportunity to start over again. As Kay Ryan remembers:

> ✳   I used to work there by myself all day long often with all these men and I was never once afraid of any of them. I felt safe and I had no fear of them though they were all alcoholic. I valued these people and they valued me in return. They were never abusive or hostile to me.   ✳

The Foundation of Charity House
Jim and Kay Ryan were the backbone of Charity House. Along with Fr. Paul they ran it for ten years with the help of volunteers. Jim Ryan devoted his entire life to Charity House and Brentwood. He took an early retirement from his place of employment, sold his home in Emeryville and moved into an apartment at Charity House with his wife Kay. They committed themselves to being involved full time. Fr.

Paul at this time still had his parish and was not able to devote his full attention to Charity House. They worked untiringly twelve to fifteen hours per day. Theirs was truly a "labor of love" since neither of them received any financial remuneration for their efforts for a good many years since there were no government funds available. They used the money from their home to make ends meet. Their devotion was based solely on their tremendous admiration, love and respect for Fr. Paul and his unselfish dedication to the suffering alcoholics. Furthermore, his enthusiasm for his mission with the alcoholic was contagious. They had an undaunted faith in Fr. Paul and his philosophy. As Kay Ryan states:

> ✳   His care and concern for the outcast led him to open Charity House for those people who had no one to care for them. Father Paul had made such an impact in our lives in three years, that we asked if we could help him in this new work. Ten years and a lot of hard work later we opened Brentwood, a Recovery Home for Alcoholics.   ✳

Jim and Kay Ryan survived because of their impassioned love and fervor. Both Jim and Kay did all the counselling, attending to the funding and all the details necessary to ensure that the program ran effectively. As Fr. Paul so strongly affirms:

> ✳   Had it not been for the unwavering commitment of both Kay and Jim neither Charity House nor Brentwood would ever have gotten off the ground. I have always emphasized this point in any recognition of Charity House or Brentwood and I am absolutely convinced that I could never have started either program without their motivation, effort integrity and perseverance. They have poured their very heart and soul into this recovery process.   ✳

The kinship, the allegiance and loyalty which has been fostered through the years between Fr. Paul and the Ryans reaches far beyond sappy sentimentalism or nostalgic melodrama. Their enduring experience is best reflected when Jim and Kay remark:

> ✳   Through the hardships and tribulations, we formed a strong bond of friendship and association that was to sustain us through thick and thin over the years. This friendship has been tested many times and has never been broken. The mutual reverence and esteem has been enduring and steadfast and has been enriched through the years.   ✳

One is able to get a clearer sense of the deep investment made by the Ryans and what it came to mean to them, both at Charity House and at Brentwood through the insights gained from Jim himself:

✳   Kay prompted me to get involved following a Sunday Liturgy where Fr. Paul had announced that he could use some volunteers to start Charity House. I agreed and decided to go down and give him my time for a day. Ironically, I've been involved ever since. Though I was a little skeptical at the start as to whether or not this project would get off the ground, the more I became engrossed in it, the more I saw the need for such a service. The more I went back the more I became enthused and the more I wanted to be "part of." Kay then became excited about it as well. As time went on, we completely renovated the entire Charity House building inside. This took all of my evenings and all of my weekends. Nonetheless, my family and I kept at it and we got more and more interested. Our children became curious and fascinated about this ambitious undertaking and the whole family really came to enjoy it. It put something very precious and valuable in our lives. In the early beginning we were getting along fine and everything was going great, but we began getting kind of complacent. We wanted more.

Fr. Paul had an unbeatable spirit where he simply would never give up on anything. He was a fighter at heart. We would ask: "Can we do it?" And he would say: "We are *going* to do it. There was no such thing as *can we* or *can't we*." Fr. Paul's enthusiasm rubbed off on us as a family *and we simply went with it.*   ✳

Eventually Kay and Jim talked about the possibility of Jim's retirement from work. He was making a good salary as a foreman and had been working for 30 years with the same company. It was determined that they would have to cut down their expenses to make ends meet and that by selling their home in Emeryville they would have a sufficient income without jeopardizing their children's welfare or anything else for that matter. They spoke to the children who were all self-supporting and who said: "That's great, we're for it"!

After selling their home in Emeryville, they immediately moved into an apartment above Charity House with no rent to pay and, as a result, were able to manage rather comfortably. Kay became heavily involved in the whole enterprise and Fr. Paul was able to convince her to become the secretary and bookkeeper. This way both Jim and Kay were actively involved in Charity House on a daily basis.

The Organization of Charity House

In the very beginning, the alcoholics were left on their own a great deal because most places like Charity House were, at the time, more widely known as hostels. They would have to leave the building during the day and either look for work or simply manage on their own and they came back in the late afternoon for supper and would stay for the evening. Therefore it did not have the intensity of the program that is presently in place at Brentwood. Everyone in the organization was a volunteer working on a part-time basis: there were no "full-time staff." The structure of the program was not as organized and not as severe or demanding as it is now. As a result, it was necessary to be much more flexible. Fr. Paul relates the complexity of his own schedule:

> ❋   I was full-time in the parish. I generally was at Charity House either early in the morning or in the late afternoon for a good part of the Charity House experience. I basically left it up to the others who were volunteering.   ❋

Those close to him know that anything that he undertakes is usually well-organized. He had a large full-time parish at that time in Emeryville and later he moved to Most Precious Blood Church which was closer to Charity House. He came most every day to Charity House where he said Mass in the Chapel. He was actually doing two jobs.

Charity House basically demanded two things of the residents: cooperation and orderliness. Some people came simply for a place to stay and something to eat. As long as they cooperated and did not cause Charity House any trouble, nothing further was demanded of them. There was another group, however, who looked for something more permanent: they wanted help in changing their lifestyle. Charity House was very strict from the beginning as to what was expected of this latter group, namely cooperation, attendance at meetings and their taking steps to modify their behavior. This included whatever was necessary for them to change their lifestyle, such as, who they hung around with, whether they were looking for work, and where they lived. Their cooperation with the staff in this regard was required in order for them to turn their lives around.

Charity House did have a program, though it was rather primitive in comparison to the Brentwood program that is so well-established today. This was mostly due to the fact that there were only a few people who actually came into the program out of their interest in getting help. As residents they were not allowed to drink, either within the program or outside the program, while the others came more only for food or a bed for the night. What the latter did in between was not a worry because it was understood that this was "*where they were at.*" Some of the residents as well as the latter group became sober and went on to have a better life and, as a result, there were many positive outcomes as a result of the Charity House experience.

Learning to Cope with the Alcoholic

Fr. Paul undoubtedly has a great affinity for dealing with wounded people. Therefore, it was not so much a matter of coping with them. Those who came for help just seemed to have a tremendous respect for Fr. Paul right from the start. In the beginning it may have been simply because he was a priest that they had this regard, esteem and admiration for him. In fact even the toughest and the most difficult just came to love him. They would affectionately refer to him as the *"black angel"* at Charity House because he wore his black suit and his black fedora. As one of the ex-convicts remarked to another priest in the area at this time:

> ✳   Fr. Paul is really something else. I would do anything to help him. I have run around town to bring in food, prepare it and serve it to the guys. He's great.   ✳

Fr. Paul seemed to understand the tremendous importance of honesty and respect in dealing with alcoholics:

> ✳   I had no difficulty because of the basic need of honesty and respect. This was always one of the most important ingredients in my life—to be honest and to practically demand honesty from people. I strived for this in my own struggle and in my own individual growth. The basic need of the alcoholic is honesty. It is what AA insists upon and what the recovering alcoholic demands in his own life in dealing with the other alcoholic. This basic premise fitted in very neatly with my own philosophy of life.   ✳

What the alcoholic needs is friendship or comradeship as well as a great deal of hope. Most of them have come from the depths of despair with little sense of ambition or aspiration. They were rejected by their own families and were strictly on their own with *nothing* and *nobody*. Fr. Paul offered them a haven at Charity House. It was something that they never had and they were given an opportunity once again to experience a sense of family—an essential ingredient which Fr. Paul always emphasized. They never would have had a Christmas had it not been for Charity House. As Kay Ryan humorously recollects:

> ✳   We used to give up our Christmas day to be there with them. We had our own Christmas the day before the 25th so that we could go to Charity House and serve the meal for these people where they could experience a sense of family. Charity House became a gift to them and it was offered at a time when they had nothing, especially at the most seasonal and most festive time of the year. The volunteers at Charity House shared and extended their own peace and joy with these people out of gratitude for what was given to them in their own lives.
> Fr. Paul and I would go and do the shopping just before Christmas and I recall going to a local department store where we were buying one hundred and twenty-five pairs of heavy wool socks because we always had about that amount of people on Christmas Day who would come to Charity House and they would get socks, a pack of cigarettes, candies and some sort of gift. The cashier

said: "My goodness! What on earth are you going to do with all those socks?" And Father Paul jokingly replied: "Oh, we just have a large family." I was just so flustered at this and he was taking it all in stride. He always had this uncanny sense of humor about life and different incidents which would occur.

Fr. Paul always had an undaunting *faith* that things would work out okay. He never worried about things and this rubbed off on the rest of us. It all seemed that whatever our needs were, they would be met at the appropriate time. I gained a lot of insights from him in this regard.   ✻

Fr. Paul's Talks at Charity House

Talks were given by Fr. Paul at Charity House but they were not all that frequent. There were not that many men on program at the time but mostly volunteers and the few residents, some of whom were not involved twenty-four hours a day. The talks actually became more organized and intense when the move was made to Sandwich Street where there was a concentrated group of people who were all there for the same reason.

The Medical Ailments of the Charity House Clientele

The amazing thing about so many of these alcoholics who came to Charity House is that they would look terribly distraught from the outside but it seemed they had grown so accustomed to living with their aches and pains that it got to a point where it did not really bother them. They did not "baby" themselves and they despised hospitals and doctors. Charity House never encountered any serious problems with the alcoholics: if any of the alcoholics had such difficulties they tended to keep it to themselves. No one ever had to be rushed to the hospital. Most of them had physical or emotional problems of course and they relied at that time on Dr. Ken Rock who made a tremendous contribution with the alcoholic. He never charged Charity House for his services and he would come whenever he was needed. He was a bulwark for Charity House.

The Financial Management of Charity House

Charity House depended on the goodwill of people. In the beginning, there was never any worry about anything because the needs were always met. Charity House managed basically with donations from organizations and churches. Almost every day was covered by some place in the city. The United Church was a great sponsor of Charity House on a regular basis. Food was donated frequently from restaurants. For a period of time, various charitable organizations would also provide a particular meal on a specific day. There were regular pickups on a certain day from them as well as such establishments as Mario's, Kentucky Fried Chicken, the Elmwood Casino, the Coboto Club, Hotel Dieu Hospital, and often the Cleary Auditorium. Bread was supplied daily by

Colombo Bakery. In this way, certain meals were assured on specific days and on other days meals were provided through Charity House funds. Charity House served two meals daily to 125 people and lodged 50 men each night. It was also involved in taking groceries to families.

The Department of Social Services began to pay Charity House $1.50 a day per meal after being in operation for two years and after it had proven that it was fulfilling a basic need in the local community. The needs of Charity House were always met without exception.

No one ever had to pay in either Charity House or Brentwood on Sandwich street. Payments were asked only at Brentwood on Dougall due to the cost of running such a program and because of the pressure from the government and the community who insisted that it would be a good idea for the residents to pay.

The Memorable I.O.O.F. Bank Loan

It was not very long before Charity House outgrew its restaurant that it became necessary to look for another facility. This was no easy feat considering the lack of money. A large building owned by the Independent Order of Foresters (I.O.O.F.) was available for purchase. In order to acquire the building, it was necessary to accept the help and support of a good number of people. Charity House was able to obtain a $25,000 bank loan on the basis of being cosigned by Bishop Carter, then Bishop of the Diocese of London. This loan, though a small beginning, was essential in order to buy the centre part of a three-sector building. Eventually, Charity House was able to buy the whole structure. Churches and organizations of various denominations donated their time and money and the City Council gave a grant of $7,500. Women's organizations held showers, bingos, card parties and other functions to supply bedding, towels and other items necessary for a 50-bed hostel.

Charity House and Formalized Religion

Formalized religion was never brought into Charity House nor is it brought into Brentwood because it would be wrong to try to impose a religious belief on victims of alcoholism who seek treatment. Moreover, the majority of those in treatment not only would be turned off by such an approach, but the whole structure would be suspect by the larger community. People go to Brentwood to get help with their alcoholism, which was the contract Charity House honored and which Brentwood continues to honor.

The Transition from Charity House
to Brentwood by the River

Charity House did have a program for those who wanted to be rehabilitated. The philosophy was *never to turn anyone away* and the doors were open for everyone without exception. Charity House never had a waiting list; it didn't believe in it. Rather, if an alcoholic got up the courage to come for help, it was felt he needed that help immediately.

To be told to come back in a week when a bed was available made it all the more likely that the alcoholic would never return.

If possible, the goal was to rehabilitate all who sought help and make them better members of society. Charity House accomplished this task to a visible degree. After a lengthy period of time social services started to provide for these people, which was the reason that Charity House was no longer needed. The single men who were not able previously to get welfare were now getting some assistance. It was first noticed that the numbers diminished when the men received their pay from welfare at the beginning of the month because they had money and would not come for help. They bought their food and had places to live. But toward the end of the month, when the money was low, they would return. Besides those on the streets, there were a good number of mothers with children who came, much like the Downtown Mission experiences today. Charity House not only dealt with alcoholics but with people who had other needs as well.

After ten years in operation, the government then came in and asked Fr. Paul to start a recovery home. According to Jim Ryan, they wanted the three of them to be involved. This was in conjunction with the detox unit which was one of sixteen to be opened in the province for the chronic drunken offender. To his dismay, Fr. Paul was required to leave the present structure since the government insisted that the next facility be a home-like structure. They wanted Fr. Paul to sell the original building and to choose a more appropriate residence, a recovery *home*, not a recovery *house* or *building*. At this particular moment in time Fr. Paul was not very pleased with their suggestion and refused to go along: he, Jim and Kay knew full well how hard they had worked to create and maintain Charity House and they were convinced that they could accomplish just as much where they were.

One Sunday the three of them were out for a leisurely drive and they passed a large house at 3020 Sandwich Street which was for sale. It was owned by the sisters of St. Joseph. At first glance, they could readily see the tremendous possibilities this place had for the start of a recovery home as it was simply irresistible.

The sisters knew Fr. Paul and they were very much in favor of converting their facility into a recovery home rather than selling it to anyone else. But it was difficult to purchase the building because Charity House lacked the necessary cash for a down payment. So Kay and Jim contributed some of their own money as did Fr. Paul.

Following this the government examined the facility themselves and concluded: "This is exactly the type of structure we want. We see this as a viable recovery home." They determined that for the population of Windsor, the facility would hold a maximum of 20 alcoholics which meant 20 beds. After a great deal of difficulty, the purchase was made.

But this was only the beginning of their problems and anxieties. The move into 3020 Sandwich Street required that Brentwood meet all of the code requirements for the City of Windsor and this proved to be both extensive and expensive requiring them to borrow additional money from the bank. And although they finally were able to get City approval, the government funding did not come for quite some time. In the meantime, Fr. Paul, Kay and Jim had to support this project themselves or risk going under financially. Finally, they started to receive funding from the government by means of a per diem rate for each resident.

In addition to the government referrals, Brentwood was receiving referrals from detox. Jim would originally go over to detox and interview each individual there and see what his intentions were in terms of possibly coming to Brentwood. "Did he just want shelter, or did he want to do something about his problem"? Eventually they had reached the allotted quota of 20 people. Referrals were still coming at an increasing rate. At one time there were numerous self-referrals where people would just walk in on their own and say: "I think I need help." Jim would subsequently talk to them and refer them to Fr. Paul who interviewed all the people who walked in off of the street.

As to leaving Charity House and the people who received aid at 634 Chilver Road, Fr. arranged with the newly opened Downtown Mission to take care of them. This set the focus for the transition from Charity House to what later became known as *Brentwood on Sandwich Street*. Charity House had accomplished its mission: it did what it had set out to do and there was a certain degree of relief in knowing that the government provided for those who had been in its care. It was thus relatively easy for Fr. Paul, Jim and Kay to make the change. Fr. Paul was appointed to Brentwood full-time in June of 1977 by Emmett Carter, then Bishop of London, who was soon to be named Archbishop of Toronto and a Cardinal of the Roman Catholic Church.

Jim Ryan: Jack-of-all-Trades

Jim Ryan was not only part of the backbone of Brentwood, he was very much involved in all aspects of the daily operation of the facility. Jim was the indispensable handyman of Brentwood who did everything needed from nursing, counselling and repairing to contracting with alumni for free professional help. In his own words:

✳   I always felt: "You can't cure people with a building." I have been more interested in the physical aspects of the facility, its repairs, upkeep and so on. Although I did counselling and I did different things, I was more or less the jack-of-all-trades. At one time I was the nurse, the plumber, you name it, I was everything. Whatever needed doing. I learned a lot in the process. I was always convinced that I had to keep the physical structure intact and in a healthy condition. There were people who were more capable of doing the counselling and so on. I ended up doing what I was good at doing and what I actually enjoyed doing the most. I could always depend on the alumnae to give me a helping hand.

The alumnae are fantastic, and that's really what Brentwood is—the alumnae. If you don't have the alumnae, all you have is a building where people pass through and they're gone. They show their gratitude by coming back. They are all interested. We have enough to keep the ball rolling. At any given time, no matter what profession it is, if we require it, we have it in the alumnae. We don't have to go outside the alumnae because we have lawyers, doctors, teachers, social workers, engineers, construction people, trades people and so on.   ✳

Anecdotes

In the twenty-five years, Brentwood would sometimes have real *characters* who would come in, some wanted to "kill" someone and some wanted to "con" others out of money (which some managed to do). One chap by the name of Johnnie was a lovable guy who actually had coined Fr. Paul as the "Black Angel" because of his priestly garb and because of the spiritual work he was doing with the men. He called another staff the "Enforcer" because he was the man who made the residents go to the various meetings. This Johnnie was involved with the mob and what-not. Christmas was coming up and he went with Norm who was on the board of directors. They were going to do some Christmas shopping. Johnnie did not have a dime but merely went along to help Norm. When they got out of the department store Johnnie opened his coat and showed Norm: "Look at the Christmas presents that I have for the guys on program." He had stolen everything he went by in the store because he had been shoplifting. Norm made him return and put it back, but Johnnie retorted: "Norm! It's harder to put it back than it is to take it." Nonetheless, he did put it back.

Another incident actually could have turned out to be a *tragedy*. Two AA men had brought a chap into the house one evening around supper time who was in horrible shape. He was hallucinating and going through the DTs. A resident by the name of Franco sat with him all night since he was warned not to let him out of his sight. So this new resident was simply hyper. He did not want to be there and was all over the place. So finally he broke out of one room, ran down the hall screaming his head off, went into another room, and dove out the window. And if his toes had not caught on the window sill he would have fallen right on the cement but his toes caught and he landed on a big schrub and all he received was a sprained ankle but he could have been killed. So we called the police and the ambulance and they took him to dry out. He sued us several years later. This was settled out of court.

In putting up the Christmas tree one could always be sure to have twenty or twenty-five people giving advice on how it should be done. This was quite a big family to put a tree up for. The trimming of the tree was actually therapeutic because it helped to bring some of the men out of their fear and loneliness. They got involved and they felt that they were helping. We never let a Christmas go by without them getting a gift.

Christmas was always a sad time of year for the alcoholic who remained in residence since it is at this time that they got in touch with their feeling lonely—and all this without the booze or the drugs. It was the time where one could feel the melancholia and depression set in. The staff did their best to try and fill that gap but it was a very depressing time for the alcoholic because he wanted to be anywhere except in a recovery home, but he had no other place to go. Consequently, it was very difficult for the staff to be of help to them at this time because of the depth of their depression. Kay was always good at this since she was seen as the warm nurturing mother. Some of the men who were older than her were referring to her as "mother." She was their connection with what they had lost. She was excellent at providing this warm acceptance and it gave the men a chance to lead them back into the sense of family. By the time the end of Christmas Day came about, they would be back in good spirits.

This anguish and discomfort was understandable with the alcoholic's bleak sense of the future and memories of a lost past. They missed what they didn't have because they were the ones who forfeited it all and some had a difficult time finding any hope in either the present or the future. When they got into the feelings they realized that they were accountable for their past and this was felt with a terrible degree of lament and grief. Those who had parents and loved ones were also very much aware that those close to them were not going to forgive them simply because it was Christmas. As a result they could actually have become more angry and agitated. With everyone helping out, the staff were able to see the transformation and they could see how well they felt inside. It was quite a chore to get them out of it.

Keeping In Touch

According to Jim, keeping in touch with the male alumnae is a very important task:

✳ Brentwood has touched a lot of people, and a lot of people have touched me. One of the rewards of being involved in Brentwood has been the feedback from the alumnae. In fact, I just got a beautiful letter from an alumnus who now lives in Scotland. When he came into Brentwood at forty-five years of age he had concluded: "My career is over, life doesn't mean anything to me. I'm done, I've had it." He had been an entertainer and we told him that his life was merely beginning. We got him to list the positives in his life. So, sure enough, he did. He graduated and before we knew it he was back in his field of entertainment. He decided to go home to Scotland and he has since gotten married. In fact I got a letter yesterday and his wife just had a baby. He feels great. When you get somebody coming back and saying: "Jim,

Brentwood has really helped me," and I get a lot of that, it feels really good. Miracles never cease and he hasn't touched booze since. This to me is one of the real success stories.

Another story involves a man named Bobby. This sticks out distinctively in my mind because he came into the program with such a defeated attitude. Fr. Paul advised him to simply *hang in there* and things would right themselves. He discouragingly said at first: "It's impossible, I'm in this too deep." Though he thought he was hopeless, we were able to give him the encouragement to go on. He had a lot of people helping him in addition to Brentwood. This is a man who had a high community profile combined with prestige, honor and status. He had everything including his Scottish pride to go along with it. He was well-known and respected in his profession and was well-to-do financially. But while he was at Brentwood, he was put on an allowance of twenty dollars a week. Here was a man who made thousands yet who had to humble himself by asking me each week for his twenty dollars.

There are several other success stories. One chap lived in a flophouse downtown. This man was destitute. He had no determination. He was just beaten when he came. He looked wretched and forlorn. He had nothing but the clothes on his back. He was a very intelligent person though he had the dreadful appearance of a "skid-row bum." He was very quiet, and he had ambition, but you just couldn't bring him out. Following his effective completion of the program he regained his confidence and was able to say: "I can do it if I put my mind to it. I have got the honesty to just go ahead and do what Fr. Paul has directed." After he went through the program, he had discovered this tremendous love which he had for horses. He moved back out West where he started a horse ranch which has now grown sizably. He's really doing well and writes to me regularly. Brentwood gave him a whole new lease on life as well as a renewed conviction.   ✳

Jim is very enthused about being able to keep in touch with these people. At Brentwood he is referred to as the *foreign correspondent*, because he tries to keep contact with as many alumnae as he can. It provides a good connection for them as well as for the people at Brentwood. He writes back faithfully to people from out West, overseas, and from as far away as Australia. Jim likes to keep that contact, especially with those who are at far-off places where he can feed them a bit of news and keep them abreast of the latest developments which are happening with the program and the fellowship. What Brentwood is now doing with people from far-off places is sending them the regular Brentwood newsletter. This keeps them interested in what is going on here and it makes them feel that they belong. After all, this is where they took their first successful step into recovery. And periodically, if they are coming anywhere near Windsor, they will come with great pride to visit and make Brentwood their first stop.

Norm Shanahan's Impact on Brentwood

Norm Shanahan was a man from the streets who did not appear to have that much to offer. Because of his love of the other alcoholic and because of his own honesty and sense of humility, he was able to make many breakthroughs in helping others. He had a great deal of influence on the other alcoholic because his whole philosophy contained the spirit of what a recovered alcoholic should be. In gratitude for what was given to him and because of his deep interest and concern for the other alcoholic, he was able to know what a human being *is* and was able to become that person. He had the sensitivity and insight to treat whoever came before him with dignity and respect. He appreciated the new way of life which was afforded him and he extended this as a gift to others. He did not simply hoard it for himself but, in turn, shared it richly with others.

There are many others who have had a similar impact but Norm stands out because he did not have a job. He was around all the time. Most of the others went back to their families and returned to work or had other responsibilities that required their attention. They were only at Brentwood for a short period of time. Norm had neither a family nor a job to which to return. He was on social assistance, was free to make that kind of commitment, and was involved with Brentwood on a twenty-four-hour basis. Kay Ryan distinctly remembers Norm's first encounter with Brentwood:

✻ I can still very vividly recall the day that Norm came in. It was on a Sunday when we were eating dinner at the old Brentwood on the river. I answered the doorbell and it was him. He was picked up off the street and simply dropped off at Brentwood. He was down and out much like someone from the streets and he looked broken and despondent. I said to Father Paul: "We have a man at the door who looks like a Charity House lad." Regrettably, at first, we did not hold out much hope for this man because he just looked so pathetic and desperate.

To our amazement he ended up having a great deal to offer. From that day on, I learned a very valuable lesson of how not to judge another person at first glance. Or, as the expression goes "not to judge a book by its cover." Because some of the ones that you might think are so hopeless and will never make it, are the very ones who end up surprising you. After Norm, it really made me think twice before passing an opinion on someone merely by their physical manifestations.

Norm was like the Mounted Police—he always got his man. When Fr. Paul sent Norm out to see someone, he didn't just go out and talk to him and say: "Call me in a day or so or I'll call you." Norm actually brought the person back to Brentwood. He pursued the alcoholic much like "the hound of heaven." He just didn't give up on the drunk but always managed to bring the person back. It has always been the philosophy of Brentwood that when the alcoholic needs help he or she needs it at that precise moment. A lot of alcoholics have benefitted from Norm to the extent that he brought them in and from there Brentwood was able to rehabilitate them.   ✳

Brentwood's Expansion

Eventually, Brentwood was clearly bursting at the seams and there was simply not enough room. People were sleeping in the halls, on chesterfields or wherever they could find a resting place. According to Jim:

> ✳   Kay and I had a small apartment in Brentwood and we eventually had to move out to the back porch to free those bedrooms for more clients. I think within the building we moved three times and then finally we moved across the street because rooms were so desperately needed. Brentwood had grown then to such proportions that it was necessary to put an addition on the structure at the cost of about $15,000. This was a lot of money at the time considering Brentwood's limited budget. The addition was primarily for a meeting room but eventually was combined into both a meeting room and a dining hall.   ✳

Before too long, the Brentwood facility on the river simply was too small as the program got too big. By that time a lot of the alumnae had become actively involved and interested in Brentwood. They were coming back in a conscientious and consistent fashion. It became obvious that they had an integral part to play in the recovery process. It was then discovered that the Elmwood (a former casino) was for sale. Upon first inspection, the building seemed a total disaster: it was simply in shambles. Nonetheless, one alumnus is known to have said: "Structurally it's a sound building and there is a lot of space. There is a marked advantage in having all these rooms for the clients." With the help of alumnae who had know-how, Fr. Paul was convinced that it would work. Brentwood had the human resources in the men alumnae. As Jim Ryan remarks:

> ✳   The male alumnae were our primary asset. Without them we couldn't possibly have tackled a job that was so monumental because it was just too much. Some of the alumnae really got involved and some of them are still actively involved on the board. It took us a year to renovate this building, but it worked out beautifully. Now we are outgrowing it because we continue to expand in leaps and bounds.   ✳

The need for a larger facility is still very great though it is difficult to convince the government of this. It seems that they cannot be persuaded by the evidence before them. As Jim states:

> *   Even if you show them hard evidence like our burgeoning intake and our alumni list of four thousand or more, they still cannot be persuaded about the pressing need. Most likely we have to make ourselves more socially known in the community. Perhaps a more enhancing profile would give people a better appreciation of exactly what we are doing for the City of Windsor, the County of Essex and in some respects the province of Ontario. Extending the Brentwood perspective will put us in better stead with the government. In many ways the word is spreading that we are a viable recovery facility providing a real need and the public is starting to realize this.   *

Reminiscing on the Years at Brentwood

Jim Ryan speaks most fondly of the pleasant but also trying years which were involved at both Charity House and Brentwood for him and his family:

> *   There are a lot of good and beautiful memories here for me and I don't regret one moment of my involvement. We've had hard times and we've had struggles. We had the ups and downs to the point where it would get very discouraging. When we tended to get depressed, Fr. Paul had a knack for getting us out of it in a hurry. He would simply distract us by putting us to work or making us do something. By getting it out physically, the first thing we knew, is that we were out of our despondency, and we were fine. We were up and going again.
>
> Brentwood has brought our family closer together. I feel that in life there is always the danger of becoming complacent to the point where we get satisfied and we do nothing with ourselves. In the process, we sometimes take advantage of our families. A point is reached where one needs a challenge and Brentwood certainly has been a challenge to get me out of myself. In fact, it was a challenge that I thought I was not capable of accomplishing since I wouldn't usually take the risk. Had I not been persuaded and prompted by Kay, I might still be in the throws of my self-indulgence and self-satisfaction. I don't think I would have ever grown beyond the point of boredom and monotony. But, to get right down to it, I enjoy my own involvement now in Brentwood because my heart is in it and it makes me feel good that Brentwood is expanding. The result that is seen today has collectively been the fruit of our labor. It's been really great for our whole family. I hope to be involved here until the day I die.   *

The Impact of the Brentwood
Program on the Alumni

Alumni feel they are different in their whole approach toward life. Their lives have been enriched in a way which would never have occurred had it not been for both Fr. Paul and Brentwood. As one person remarks:

✳   Brentwood has been a pivotal point for me. In truth, I did not know what my problems were although I knew something was desperately wrong. My relationships with people were becoming more and more difficult. My wife had said: "No more game playing." I had enough program to know I needed more if I were to live properly. Brentwood restored my integrity. It has provided me with people who are committed to living out a basic set of principles: sharing, forgiving, confiding, consulting, asking, listening and following direction in order that I might take the honest, caring, responsible action.

Brentwood has shown me that I was addicted to self-defeating types of behaviour and it has involved me in a treatment program that has created a radical difference in my relation to others. The Brentwood program has put me in touch with my emotions and with the feelings of those closest to me in a depth which at times is filled with joy, at other times, with sadness and pain. That is why I realize the need for other people in my daily encounter. I could not carry these feelings alone anymore because I had severely blocked them. This disease had cut me off from my roots.   ✳

Another person summarized it succinctly by saying:

✳   Brentwood has changed my life and that of my family's for the better. It has allowed me to feel like a human being. I was dying emotionally and psychologically. Because of the ill-fated decisions which I made, I was on a "*self-destruct path*". Now, through Brentwood, I have the ability not only to respect others and care for them, but to respect and care for myself. Now I can live more whole. I no longer need to fear people as a threat or to be paranoid that people are "*out to get me*". Today I can rejoice and celebrate people as genuine gifts to me and I, in turn, can be an authentic gift to other people.   ✳

Alumni have a greater amount of patience with themselves and a better acceptance of others today. In the past, what other people were doing or not doing controlled them immeasurably. Today, they have more of an inner composure, acceptance, and commitment to carry the message of recovery to others who are still suffering from the disease. In the words of one individual:

✳   Brentwood saved my life and transformed it. It gave me a purpose, a meaning and a new freedom. It provided me with the ability to love. I never believed that my life could be so fruitful. I am looking forward to many more years because there is so much more to live for. I would not have a life today if it weren't for Brentwood. When I came here, Brentwood *did promise* me that if I *worked* the program that I would get some peace of mind, some happiness and self-worth; and that has certainly happened. It feels as if I had been lost for such a long time and now I've found myself.

Before Brentwood, I was always an immature child. Fr. Paul made me *grow up* and appreciate the beauty I had inside, a beauty which I had marred by the destructiveness of my own life. I hated myself so desperately that I refused to face the challenges that were before me. I cherish this life that I have today and I am grateful that I can share it with others.   ✳

Understanding the way alcoholics perceive things has given the alumni insight into their own lives and has helped them to cope more readily with the alcoholic and with those members of their own families. One person in particular renders a very positive account of the self-control she established in and through the Brentwood fellowship.

✳   When I came here I was a *"basket case"*. I had completely given up. My brother, a Brentwood alumnus, came through and I saw the tremendous change in him. I could hardly believe what had happened to him. For the first time in my life I had a brother with whom I could relate, who was open and caring. I was deeply impressed by what had transpired in his life as a result of his coming through the program. I did not know anything about Brentwood at the time but I came to an open meeting with the women and I got "taken up" by the whole process. There was something here that was very valuable. After a year and a half of meetings, I stayed away for six months only to realize that I *was* an alcoholic. I fought it as much as I could because I was a practicing drunk. I denied my own disease and said to myself: "They're talking about somebody else, not me."

When I got here, I was resolved to apply myself. I knew that I could not do any more with my life the way I was going. My life has been a complete change since then. Now I feel a hundred percent better.

I can see that there are reasonable solutions to issues and that I don't have to spin unnecessarily. I no longer have that sense of despair and hopelessness. I am on top of things now. I no longer have to give up on life since I have a more solid foundation. Because I have hope today, I am pleased for where I am and the progress I have made. I couldn't ask for better and I couldn't ask for more. This is *a touch of heaven* for me. I am filled with gratitude. I know the good that happens here and I am not afraid to face what each day brings. I am humbled because today I am making every effort to *walk* the program.

CHAPTER 7

The Church's Perception
of Brentwood[1]

When Cardinal Carter, Archbishop Gervais and Bishops Sherlock and Henry think of Fr. Paul's work with alcoholism and its association with the Church, numerous things come to their minds. He is seen as a most compassionate man, able to see a need among the laity as well as among his brother priests. Historically, Brentwood first opened its doors after the Second Vatican Council, at the time when students and the Labour movement were in turbulence, as indeed was the whole church. There was the misunderstanding of the freedom that Vatican II had given to the clergy and the teachings of Vatican II were misread and misrepresented. There was a big exodus from the priesthood and the religious orders and everything was upside down. Priests felt that Vatican II had downgraded them in favor of the laity. This type of attitude led to an increased incidence of alcoholism among some priests. There was more than the usual number of priests who were drinking, and some of them were thinking of leaving the priesthood.

Fr. Paul was aware of these problems. He felt very close to his brother priests and many would talk to him. Fr. Paul was the kind of priest with whom one could open up. He would never register shock. He was like a father/confessor to many of the Roman Catholic, Anglican and Protestant clergy of Windsor. He wanted to do something to help clergy and people who had this alcoholic problem, and proceeded to develop a treatment centre.

Fr. Paul had been involved in the field of alcoholism for a very long time, in fact, even prior to his ordination as a priest. He is the type of person who eagerly learns from experience. In the earlier years

---

1.   The following chapter was taken exclusively from the communication of Emmett Cardinal Carter and the three bishops who have been involved with Brentwood over the years. It indicates how strongly the institutional Church supports this work and the the enormous esteem with which they hold Fr. Paul Charbonneau as a leader in the field of alcoholism and drug rehabilitation.

he was still intensely involved in parish work while following his intuition with the alcoholics who would come to see him. He had not yet formulated a theory about alcoholism. His experience with alcohol and with alcoholics is what led him to his present awareness and skill. He expanded his theory till it became what it is today. He disciplined himself through a very vigorous and demanding learning process by carefully and painstakingly analyzing what he did, not just experiencing it but trying to evaluate his theories by sharing them with others. *The real progress came in his learning from his experience.* It was his deep sense of responding to a need which he repeatedly reflected upon through trial and error, that he embellished his approach as he went along. He would assess the practicality of his theories, assimilating only those that were successful. He had a propensity for perseverance. From the very beginning of his work, he displayed great insight. He was not only very pragmatic but he was able to theorize his accomplishments after they had been proven effective. He could abstract the reality—a process which he learned so well in the seminary. He was well-trained and reasoned from the concrete to the abstract, not from the theory to the practice. *His work with alcoholism is what made sense and gave meaning to his priesthood.* His involvement in treating the alcoholic became for him a fulfillment of his priesthood.

Fr. Paul never pities an alcoholic. He is never "mushy," "sentimental" or "lachrymose." He abhors artificial overtones and sappy melodrama which the alcoholic so well portrays. There are a number of alcoholics who, when they first meet him, don't like him; and many don't like him at the end of the program either. This is readily understandable since there are a good number of alcoholics who look for *pity* because they are living in *self-pity.* Self-pity is the last thing the alcoholic needs. At times, his approach may seem to be harsh and uncaring but it has to be seen within its proper context. Bishop Gervais makes the following observation of Fr. Paul:

> ✳ His approach is a confrontation of reality. The business of never pitying the alcoholic seems to work since in Fr. Paul's eyes to do so would only reinforce the disease. His approach is more a position of calling forth strength in the other person rather than pampering them and letting them get away with the childish and perilous behaviour which has always personified them in the past. ✳

Early Involvement of the Various Bishops with Fr. Paul and his Work

Fr. Paul was not the typical priest. He had some splendid connections. Whatever he chose to do, there would be an enormous amount of moral support and eventually that began to translate into financial support. Fr. Paul had deep roots in the Windsor community. He had not only a strong lineage from childhood but the Charbonneau family is related to a wide variety of people in Windsor and Essex County. The clergy however, backed him for the most part even though they were both amused and somewhat unconvinced. In fact they exhibited a strange blend of commitment on the one hand and they would say: "Well, that's Fr. Paul." At one point, Fr. Paul was chosen unanimously as the Dean of Windsor. He had been elected by his peers—a sign of a great deal of trust and confidence. His fellow priests considered him a *natural leader* and one whom they thought was competent to call together the priests and preside over their meetings. Having been the dean, he had the support of his fellow pastors and the assistant priests and was well-known, admired and liked.

His Eminence, Cardinal Carter, sees alcoholism as a very serious matter since we are in what some knowledgeable people maintain is an "addicted society." In the early '60s, Fr. Paul asked his Eminence, Emmet Cardinal Carter, then Bishop of London if he might be freed from his pastoral assignments so that he could work with alcoholics.

Fr. Paul's response to the plight of alcoholism has always been very direct. He initially saw the need and responded to it and as he was attempting to do so, realized very quickly that it required a full time commitment. The Bishop at that time, in consultation with his personnel committee, judged that this was the appropriate thing to do. It is not very often that the bishop feels free to release a priest who clearly has outstanding leadership abilities to a totally new and unprecedented kind of discipline. Cardinal Carter, who made the final determination at the time, was also a daring and innovative individual, which probably accounts for the courageous intrepidity of his decision. Fr. Paul was a dedicated pastor who worked well beyond the call of duty and did more than was necessary as a priest. He was regarded as a good solid diocesan priest who would be hard to replace. Having accepted Fr. Paul's general objectives, the Church at this point, through its ecclesiastical approval, gave its formal sanction and blessing to Fr. Paul for his dedication to the field of alcoholism. Without his full-time leadership in the area of alcohol rehabilitation, the kind of development he was hoping for would not have taken place. It is believed that Brentwood exists predominantly because Fr. Paul is the driving force behind it with its alumni and secondly, because it successfully meets a need. As Bishop Sherlock remarks:

* It could never have been there without the kind of leadership which some would describe as reckless but I would describe as absolutely determined. The goal was the important thing for him and the means would be found—*and eventually they were*. It is rather ludicrous and preposterous to think that in a province where most rehabilitation clinics are highly funded by government and where there are very limited caseloads on the part of all the counsellors, that this enormous operation started with no funding whatever, except what came from donations and bingo. *

Fr. Paul was appointed to Brentwood full-time in June of 1977 by Emmet Cardinal Carter, then Bishop Carter. As Auxiliary Bishop, and as part of the personnel committee, Bishop John Michael Sherlock participated very directly with Cardinal Carter in making the decision that Fr. Paul be released from his parish duties and responsibilities. It was felt that Fr. Paul might well use his talents more productively in the field of alcoholism than in parish work since he had a driving commitment to be involved in this area. Fr. Paul was perceived as having a panoramic view of issues as well as a microscopic perception of detail, and as one who could cut through numerous technicalities: the marks of an excellent administrator.

Bishop Gervais was also on the personnel committee of the diocese when he knew that Fr. Paul was asking to be appointed into full-time work with alcoholics. He had complete confidence in him right from the start and actually claimed to be *prejudiced in his favor*. As he comments:

>   *   Not everyone likes Fr. Paul. I happen to like him. There is a genuineness about him: he isn't phoney. He could be irritating at times. Before he found himself in Brentwood, he was a maverick in many ways. He was an "agitator." He was always on the muscle, not knowing what he was angry about—like a rebel without a cause. He was simply against authority. And, ironically, right now he is at the very heart of authority in his role as executive director of Brentwood. There was always something real about him. When he got channelled into alcoholism, it was irreversible. It was a breakthrough for him in the sense that he became more pleasant and understanding. There was an inner peace which had unfolded within him.   *

Bishop Fred Henry speaks of the quality of Fr. Paul's work in the field of alcoholism:

>   *   I can very much appreciate where he is coming from and I do have confidence in him. I believe that what Fr. Paul is doing is really spiritual. Basically, he is saving people on two levels. He is saving them *physically* and he is saving them *spiritually*. His mission is truly the mission of a disciple. I'm convinced of this because of what he says and what he has done for others. He has saved some of them from physical death and he has restored them spiritually.   *

Obviously all of the church leaders involved had nothing but the highest regard for Fr. Paul's leadership in the area of alcoholism. As Bishop Sherlock remarked:

>   *   My appreciation of his endeavour is high. Fr. Paul is using his creative skills within the Church now in an obviously clerical

way by working with the people of God. He has exceptional leadership abilities and a deep concern for people with alcoholic problems.   ✳

Perception of Fr. Paul as a Priest

Cardinal Carter sees Fr. Paul as a very good priest who has a very strong mind of his own. As he remarks:

> ✳   So he is not a "Yes" man by any stretch of the imagination. But when Fr. Paul does not agree with you, he simply tells you he doesn't agree with you. Nonetheless, if the bishop said something, he obeyed. He is not a person who would say one thing in front of you and another behind your back. He is very upright. He is never overly critical of authority. If he has anything to criticize he does it directly to authority, which is a rather admirable quality that I respect very highly.   ✳

Fr. Paul was the kind of person who could establish an immediate contact especially if he could see one's honesty. If he knew you and you were not phoney with him, he would not play games with you. It would be straight talk. This is something that could always be appreciated about him. As Bishop Gervais recalls:

> ✳   I always admired him as a young priest and looked up to him. There was something very genuine about him. I never had a feeling of despising him. I may disagree with some of the things he said and so on, but I always had a basic liking for him as a priest. He was a priest right through, with no obfuscation, no attempt to muddle, confuse or go around things. There was no contradiction in him as a person or as a priest; these roles were both unified. He completely integrated his uniqueness into his priesthood. When he spoke as a priest, it was not just theory or something out of his head. There were no facades. "What you see is what you get."   ✳

His Eminence Emmet Cardinal Carter spoke very fondly of his rapport with Fr. Paul: "We always had a good relationship, Fr. Paul and I. Sometimes, he could be critical but I always considered him a friend and a good person." Bishop Sherlock was able to say: "He is an honest, direct and forthright man who retains a most vivid sense of humor. He can be kidded and he does not take himself or anything else too seriously. I enjoy him and admire him very much." Bishop Gervais laments that he is no longer in Windsor with Fr. Paul:

> ✳   I enjoyed being close to him and rubbing shoulders with him. One thing that strikes me is Fr. Paul's work with native people who are alcoholic. He has a fairly high degree of success with native people. There is a kind of missionary feature to the message

and the method that he has. I couldn't be any more in favor of his work. In addition to the brotherly love and close admiration I have for Fr. Paul I sense him as someone who is close to God in and through his closeness to people. Fr. Paul has really fleshed out the message of the gospel in the true sense of the term.   ✳

Fr. Paul's Straightforwardness

According to the church leaders Fr. Paul has always been known to be *blunt* and *direct.* Nonetheless, he can always be trusted in what he says. His words always carry conviction and certainty.

The job of the priest, modelled on Christ, is to draw the community together usually through the word, but also through love and compassion. What he is doing in terms of the Gospel is more than justified as *priestly work.* He draws people together in a spirit of love and healing. And this is essentially and eminently priestly work. Though others can do this, it takes a very special priestly character to *build up community* the way he does. He fleshes out the message of the Gospel and attempts to heal the pain associated with alcoholism. He heals communities, restores families; and all this radiates abundantly through a whole community or a parish. He is totally open in terms of dealing with people in need. Though he has his successes and his failures, Fr. Paul is prepared to take enormous risks. As in scripture, he is willing to lose his life and to risk loving in order that others might have life and "have it more abundantly."

Fr. Paul's risk-taking is exemplified in his daily talks at Brentwood when he stands before a full assembly of residents and alumni, including lawyers, university professors, bikers, ex-cons, priests and winos or street people who are all at Brentwood for one purpose—recovery. He absorbs himself in the world of the other "drunk" where incarnation, redemption and salvation are possible and this in effect, is the fundamental issue of the Gospel.

The key factor is his honesty and integrity. His direct line is to attack the problem head-on because basically the alcoholic is a dishonest person. When one is confronted by an honest person, one can be sure that *the sparks are going to fly.* One can see this in his thinking.

Fr. Paul has a marvelous way of getting across the fundamental gospel message without sounding pietistic or overly religious. His approach is reminiscent of Jesus' approach when he was preaching as he sat on the grass and spoke simply to the people where they were, both geographically and emotionally. Fr. Paul too has this gift. In speaking to people, he uses everyday language that they can grasp and understand. Sometimes the language might seem crude and rough but when one considers what he is actually saying, Fr. Paul's message is clearly a reflection of the basic message of the gospel which he has applied most appropriately to our times.

Fr. Paul's ability to speak the truth is legendary and it has always been a truth that applies to every kind of alcoholic. Everyone comes to know that his or her relationship with Fr. Paul is a deeply private and intensely personal encounter. Never careless, he can address the total context of a person's life, both the public and the private. He also has a most ingenious way of saying things and a manner which is both inventive and creative. His whole life and practice with the alcoholic reflects what happens when *truth* comes out of *practice*.

Fr. Paul speaks the truth, even when it is uncomfortable to do so. He has always been seen as the classic type of person, with whom one knows exactly what his stand is going to be on a particular issue or question. Not the type of person to talk behind someone's back, he is always up front. But of course a person with these particular characteristics and with this singular type of approach is a great gift in one way but he can also be painfully contentious at times. In fact, the waters are not usually tranquil when Fr. Paul is around because of his ultimate honesty. However, out of the pain of Fr. Paul's rigorous honesty comes his tremendous insightfulness which is so characteristic of the Brentwood atmosphere. Fr. Paul is a zealot with a strong sense of balance in his life. As a determined zealot he is bound to provoke opposition as well as disapproval.

CHAPTER 8

Fr. Paul's Management Style[1]

Wilfred A. Gallant and Forrest C. Hansen

In this chapter we will speak to two issues, the first on the charismatic qualities of a leader and how these apply to Fr. Paul, and the second, the results of an empirical survey on him.

Fr. Paul as a Charismatic Leader

Now and again a community is endowed with a leader of singular vision who is able to gather sufficient momentum so as to make an indelible mark upon a people and its followers. Fr. Paul can be identified somewhat as a "doctor of the soul" who has lifted the human spirit and united the Brentwood people together in an enduring spirit of community while in pursuit of the most noble of all goals—*love, understanding and compassion*. Fr. Paul's charisma is due partly to his own invariable quest for unity and fellowship but it must ultimately be attributed to his vocation as a Catholic priest from which he received his theological orientation. It was on strong religious and spiritual grounds that he developed the Brentwood philosophy. His grasp of spiritual principles and his soul-searching response to his priestly ministry led him to heal the wounds of those afflicted with alcoholism as well as their families who were the victims.

At an unprecedented time in history when secular materialism is prevalent, Brentwood is a source of help to alcoholics, substance abusers and addictive personalities. The Brentwood philosophy contends that the world cannot find meaning or happiness in material possessions alone or in addictive gratification. It posits that the only way to counteract loneliness and isolation is by the genuine sharing of love, compassion and understanding with one another. Fr. Paul, through his charismatic style, created a fertile ground where authentic community

1.   The authors are grateful to J.A. Conger and R.N. Kanungo and Associates for their book: *Charismatic leadership: The elusive factor in organizational effectiveness* which has provided a timely reference which is both comprehensive and current and which is at the leading edge of this emerging field. Many of the thoughts expressed in this chapter reflect the research conducted by these authors.

was possible. He envisioned a bond between people which would provide self-realization and a deep sense of "belonging." He was instrumental in developing in alcoholics an ability to attend to and selflessly respond to the actual needs of others. "The communication we are reflecting upon is of a special kind. It is the shared gift of self with another and the constant attempt at a mutual exchange of selflessness and other-centeredness as a way of life" (McMahon & Campbell, 1967, p. 150). Fr. Paul is a charismatic leader who remains as a servant among his followers, yet whose accomplishments testify to his solitary stature and ability. He has a profound insight into the human condition and is able to lead others to fulfill their own potential.

According to Conger and Kanungo it is important to develop a theoretical foundation of charismatic leadership which relates conditions which occur *before* and *after* and which take into consideration such variables as personality, environmental conditions and subordinate behaviour. Charismatic leaders are able to motivate followers to achieve ambitious goals due to their strategic vision since they are not confined to past customs and rituals but are able to vigorously pursue unmet possibilities in their area of specialty and are able to use strategies that succeed because of their unorthodox approach (1988). With a strong emotional attraction, charismatic leaders seek to render justice to a decadent social condition. Fr. Paul's aim was to redirect, a more dynamic and precise solution to the treatment of alcoholism and addiction.

Empirical studies agree, for the most part, that charismatic leadership has a strong relational basis which "resides in the interplay between the leader's attributes and the needs, beliefs, values, and perception of followers" (Conger & Kanungo, 1988, p. 23).

In respect to the aspect of task, the social quality of a leader and the participative aspect of the followers, Conger and Kanungo postulate four variables of a charismatic leader: 1) a strategic vision, 2) risky, innovative and unconventional means, 3) a realistic assessment of environmental resources and 4) a well-articulated message. In this model the leader influences his followers through his own personal idiosyncratic power and draws from his idealized vision, his entrepreneurial advocacy for change and his unconventional expertise as the sources of his personal power. House (1977) argued that charismatic leaders possess:

> qualities of dominance, self-confidence, a need to influence, and a strong conviction of their beliefs.... They are more likely to espouse appealing ideological goals and to engage in behaviours that create the impression of success and competence in followers and that arouse motives relevant to their mission's accomplishment. (p. 30)

Charismatic leaders have an overwhelming impact on the emotions and motivation of followers to the extent that it urges them to achieve what would otherwise be insurmountable tasks.

Smith (1982) measured subordinate reactions to charismatic and noncharismatic leaders and

> ...found that the followers of reputed, effective and charismatic leaders are more self-assured, report more support from their leaders, see their leaders as more dynamic, experience their work as more meaningful, have higher performance ratings, and work longer hours than do followers of noncharismatic but effective leaders. (p. 31)

And Howell (1985) "...found that charismatic leader behavior has a more positive and stronger influence on the satisfaction, performance, and adjustment of subjects" (p. 31).

Weber ([1924], 1947) "argued that charismas either fade or become institutionalized with the accomplishment of the charismatic leader's mission" (p. 32). Clark (1972) discovered five elements which guaranteed the fulfillment of the organization's ideological goals. *First,* was a powerful nucleus of believers who routinized the charisma of the leader. *Second,* a unique course of action, remarkable requirements, or an unusual method of teaching that permitted the program's embodiment. *Third,* was an outside set of believers, who provided a supporting social base. *Fourth,* involved a student subculture to faithfully transfer the philosophy from one generation to the other. *Fifth,* was maintaining a chronicle of ceremonies and events. It was through these five mechanisms that the transmission and institutionalization of the founder's charisma and mission were ensured.

In a field study of two charismatic leaders, Trice and Beyer (1986) concluded that

> ...five factors are largely responsible for successful institutionalization: (1) the development of an administrative apparatus apart from the charismatic leader that puts the leader's mission into practice; (2) the transfer of charisma through rites and ceremonies to other members of the organization; (3) the incorporation of the charismatic's message and mission into oral and written traditions; (4) the selection of a successor who resembles the charismatic founder and is committed to the founder's mission; and (5) a continued identification with and commitment to the charismatic's original mission (p. 33).... The locus of charismatic leadership resides largely in the leader's personality. His or her personal qualities are the source of his or her influence, so his or her power is not dependent on outside forces. (p. 35)

Charismatic leaders are highly esteemed (Weber, [1924] 1947). They have a strong sense of confidence and purpose and are able to express goals and ideas in such a manner that followers are psychologically receptive to them (Fromm, 1941; House, 1977). Followers are readily inspired with a strong sense of purpose due to the extraordinary influence of the charismatic leader. The followers, in some instances, become influential leaders in their own right since they have been able to transcend their usual experience (Burns, 1978; Trice and Beyer, 1986). It has been observed by countless alumni that Fr. Paul's charisma goes well beyond the inspirational and is firmly grounded in reality since he has no illusions of any false piety or misguided asceticism. The leader is able to exercise authority in a way which is acceptable to the followers.

The followers demonstrate a reverence to the exemplary qualities of the charismatic leader (Weber [1924] 1947) and attempt to emulate his behaviour (Downton, 1973). Leaders are highly motivated to influence followers. Their self-confidence and strong convictions increase their followers' trust in the leader's judgements (p. 50–51). They are alive, yet contained and at ease (Bensman and Givant 1975 and Willner, 1968). They portray a strong sense of confidence in their beliefs and actions (Hoffman and Hoffman, 1970). They are inner-directed and self-determined. They possess a powerful sense of personal and social responsibility and act upon their values and convictions (Nietzsche, [1883] 1974). Charismatic leaders are insightful in respect to problem-solving (McClelland, 1975). Charismatic leaders are able to see through people and events. They can cut through details and get to the point of things since they are relatively free of internal turmoil. With a strong sense of conviction, charismatic leaders can be straight-forward and candid not only in reprimanding subordinates but also in replacing those who need to be replaced (Keichel, 1983).

Fr. Paul: A Product of his own Crisis Resolution

The term charismatic is not being used here in a mysterious or undefinable way but is being used as "gift" which has a prophetic or healing dimension. (Conger and Kanungo, 1988, p. 21). In observing the essential combination of elements that goes into the making of a charismatic leader, the following tend to apply to Fr. Paul and give substance to the concept of charisma: extraordinary gifts; crisis; radical solution; followers who are attracted to the person and the message; followers who believe they are linked through this person to transcendent powers; repeated experiences of success; confidence building; shared vision; creating valued opportunities; call from God as in inspired leadership.

Fr. Paul's quality of spiritual growth and charisma became more and more evident through "working out" his own struggles and through his ability to make responsible decisions along the way. It is in and through the Brentwood experience that he gained the strength of his convictions and became increasingly determined to fulfill his goals and objectives with such rigor and discipline. According to Tucker (1970), the charismatic leader appears in times of crisis and followers respond with fervent loyalty because the leader promises a requisite fulfillment.

Fr. Paul was a product of his own life of crisis. His father was alcoholic and he bore the scars of an alcoholic-type personality. In his own lifetime he searched for solutions to his own identity crisis and found victory in joining the plight of those suffering from alcoholism and addiction, those who had not found a resolution to their dilemma. As he gradually moved along and experimented with his new-found approach to treating the alcoholic, he developed the model which attributes such momentum and status to his work. He came to his work honestly out of his own painful quest for the truth in his own life.

Fr. Paul's struggle was historic in that he wrestled with questions of anger and resentment in his growing years. Being "street-wise," dedication and integrity were essential ingredients among his peers. He continued to look for these qualities of loyalty and honesty in other people. He knew that the absence of these features in the alcoholic and in combination with the alcoholic's blindness and inability to love were at the heart of his own crisis situation. Fr. Paul was aware that the road to recovery required that the alcoholic become honest with himself and with others. This called for an open testimony of one's weaknesses and transgressions so as to lift the burden of guilt, remorse and despair. What Fr. Paul offered, in turn, was the compassion, love and support of the other alcoholic and his own indomitable allegiance to the process of recovery. Fr. Paul was in an ideal position to establish a charismatic mission. First, he had inherited the alcoholic traits though it was without the predominant fixation on the substance. Secondly, he had resolved his own internal conflict and was in a fitting position to be sensitive to the pain and struggle of the alcoholic without pampering or overindulgence. As Devereux (1955) expresses: "Individuals who experience crisis and feel a loss of control over their environment generally are more ready than others to accept the authority of a charismatic leader" (p. 56). Fr. Paul has been able to bring renewed intention, motivation and hope into the life of the once desperate and despondent alcoholic who has come for help.

How will Fr. Paul be Replaced?

A question is often raised as to whether or not Fr. Paul's innovative approach will endure beyond his retirement. Will the followers be able to imitate the leader, perpetuate the vision and pay allegiance to the spirit of Brentwood though it is carried on in a more institutionalized fashion? According to Conger & Kanungo (1988), "...charismatic leaders are hard acts to follow. Institutional practices and the cultural imperatives built by charismatic leaders must replace them after they are gone" (p. 58). In quoting Weber, ([1924] 1947), Conger and Kanungo state: "It must be routinized by the development of organizational rules and arrangements if it is to achieve stability". According to them, such routinization calls for some type of process to be put into place:

> First, unless a charismatic leader is replaced by an equally charismatic successor, an administrative apparatus may be created, along with rites and ceremonies, to provide continuity of message

and mission.... Second, oral and written traditions may emerge to ensure the endurance of the charismatic's effects. Third, continuity may be provided by key groups of believers, and by distinctive practices and imagery in the form of visual art, ceremonies, and stories. (p. 58, 59)

Trice and Byer (1986) found that a process of routinization occurs when examining the influence of charismatic leaders. Such a process must ensure (1) an administrative apparatus that puts the charismatic's program into practice, (2) the transfer of charisma to others in the organization, (3) the incorporation of the charismatic's message and mission into the mainstream of the organization and (4) a successor who resembles the charismatic leader and has the trust and confidence of the followers.

The Behavioural Components of Charisma

Conger and Kanungo further believe that there are clearly delineated behavioural components of charismatic leadership which are interrelated and of varying intensity. According to Conger and Kanungo this process consists of three specific stages: (1) the leader evaluates the existing situation, (2) assesses available resources, and (3) assesses the needs and level of satisfaction experienced by followers. Thus charisma is seen to function on a continuum which incorporates the span from an undesirable domain to a more desirable state. In Fr. Paul's case, it was his dismay with the lack of adequate programs to meet the intensity of service delivery required to deal with the problems of the alcoholic, the addictive personality and dysfunctional family patterns, which motivated him to embark on his model of recovery.

Fr. Paul was very much aware of the service deficiencies in terms of alcoholism recovery in the local area and of the immense need of those who were so afflicted and he was able tentatively to identify a strategic vision, often characterized by charismatic leaders, which would draw people to his style and manner of accomplishing a task. His innovative approach was a combination of his unique perception of spiritual principles which were grounded in the pain and reality of the alcoholic's bitter experience with life and his undaunted courage to forge ahead in a cogent and solitary manner. Happily, he was able to develop a model which would reach the ravaged and devastated state of the people in their disease and raise them to heights which they never dreamed possible. He was then able to alter his strategy as he went along, refining particular aspects as he deemed them necessary. Fr. Paul remained steadfast in his relentless determination to follow his hunch though his approach was perceived by others as innovative and unconventional.

One of Fr. Paul's outstanding characteristics is his sense of balance between the *ideal* and the *real*. He doesn't seek perfection from his followers but a modicum of self-worth and a basic ability to live the principles of recovery and spiritual growth. He is also able to provide a balance between the multitude of emotions and opinions which come from such a large number of people and is able to delve into the sometimes conflicting concerns of the fellowship with both patience and insight.

Fr. Paul is able to make a very resolute appraisal of deficiencies in the organization which requires attention or change. He always had a certain restlessness with inadequacies within the system which made it opportune for him to develop a radical approach to alcoholism recovery.

Fr. Paul's Charismatic Nature[2]

Fr. Paul is recognized by the Church hierarchy as a charismatic person with immense leadership capacity. The tenor of their view of him was that he is able to see an objective clearly and throw himself energetically into his work, thereby, drawing other people along with him like a driving force or a current. He draws people to energize their own inner light. Also, there is an admirable sincerity about him. He is quite different from most other priests in the fact that he is blunt, daring, direct, forceful, determined and committed. He has a dedication to people and a concern for their real needs. He has this tremendous capacity to get to the real issues.

Further, they affirmed that Fr. Paul's true leadership qualities were brought to life through the alcoholic and any charisma that is attributed to him is an endowment from those who have undergone the process of recovery and who pledge an allegiance to his philosophy. It was the alcoholic who brought out the leadership in Fr. Paul and made him a leader.

Fr. Paul's Perception

Fr. Paul is reluctant to attribute any element of charisma to his role, charisma meaning a person who has a vision, who puts into practice a model and is able to gather other followers. The bishops thought Fr. Paul to be charismatic, not in a pentecostal sense, but much like a Lee Iacocco or a René Leveque or some of the presidents of the United States. It would seem Fr. Paul disavows any element of charisma within himself. In his own words:

> ✳   I don't think I had a vision. And I don't see myself as charismatic. I just see myself as a hard-working person who feels he has to be on the job every day and still feels the need to be there for people. I don't see myself much more than that. I think the basic thing is the sheer willingness and ability to be *honest* and to *demand honesty from people*. This, in my eyes, is what produces results and probably the respect from others. Others might use adjectives such as charismatic but I don't use such adjectives to

---

2.   The following derives from my interviews with three bishops and a cardinal who are all familiar with Brentwood and Fr. Paul and conveys a collective perception of Fr. Paul as a charismatic leader.

describe myself. The bottom line for me is for people to go back to nature and the basic principles, and if one follows these through one remains true to oneself and one's nature. This calls forth honesty in ourselves and honesty in others. I can't see where there can be any lasting trust or respect unless there is absolute honesty between two people. This has always been so important for me personally and *I try to instill this honesty as the backbone and foundation of Brentwood*. I think this type of honesty inspires a great deal of loyalty. As a result of this a grea deal of respect is generated among the Brentwood fellowship. This is what is necessary in forming an organization, a community or any form of leadership.   ✳

An Empirical Perspective[3]

Conger and Kanungo who had developed a questionnaire for charismatic leadership suggested, in reference to this investigation, that it might be valuable to use their measurement scale. Consequently, the questionnaire was used to determine if Fr. Paul would be perceived by staff and alumni as a charismatic leader.

Conger and Kanungo developed this scale by operationalizing the behaviours associated with charismatic leadership. They then went to four specific organizations and asked staff members to rate their management personnel on those 29 items. On this scale, when the scores on the 29 items were summated the result was an average (mean) of 123.81 with a standard deviation of 14.79.

The Method

The purpose of this study was twofold: (1) to determine if Fr. Paul Charbonneau was perceived as a charismatic leader by the staff and alumni of Brentwood using the applied questionnaire and (2) to determine if this business orientated questionnaire could be applied to a human service organization.

Design of Questionnaire

This study was composed of two parts: (1) the questionnaire operationalizing the behavioral components of charismatic leadership. Part I comprised the Conger-Kanungo (C-K) scale of charismatic leadership and consisted of 29 behavioural components. The rating scale ranged from 1 = least characteristic to 6 = most characteristic. (2) the questionnaire comprised of the demographic characteristics.

---

3.   The authors are indebted to Dr. Jay Conger and Dr. Rabindra N. Kanungo for their article: A behavioural measure of charismatic leadership in organizations (1990) from which the authors modelled the organization and the structure for presenting the Brentwood study.

Procedure
It is estimated that in the twenty-five years that Brentwood has been in existence over five thousand alumni have gone through the program. The objective of this study was to obtain between 150 to 200 responses. The respondents included staff, current alumni, who were all former graduates, spouses of alumni, and women from the various groups at Brentwood. The respondents were asked in the beginning instructions to think of Fr. Paul Charbonneau as a person having leadership abilities and to assess their perception of him based on the prescribed questions.

Sample
The questionnaire was given to what was determined to be a purposeful sample of approximately 350 eligible respondents whom the researcher knew were associated with Brentwood and who knew Fr. Paul Charbonneau well enough to reply to the questions. Participation was voluntary and all replies were confidential. The final count revealed that 155 completed questionnaires were returned which was an approximate response rate of 45%. The response rate was considered to be a reasonably high response rate given the procedure used. Sixty-seven percent have been involved with Brentwood for less than nine years.

Results

Summary of Demographic Characteristics
The following demographic characteristics are a result of the personal data questions that were asked:

The average age was 41.5 years. Almost 65% ranged in age from thirty to forty-five. The youngest respondent was 22 and the oldest was 65. The respondents were involved with Brentwood for a period ranging from one year to twenty-five years. The average for length of involvement was 5.13 years.

Sixty-nine percent were male and 30.5% were female. The large number of males is attributed to the fact that for the first twenty years Brentwood provided a live-in-program for men and the women's program was only initiated in 1985.

Respondents were either alumni (107); women who belonged to the women's group (21), group leaders (9), counsellors (7), residents (5); or staff (1). Eighty percent of the respondents were alumni.

In terms of the marital profile, fifty-two percent were married, 16 percent were single, 28 percent were either separated or divorced and 4 percent were engaged. The single category did not specify whether or not the respondents had been previously married.

Their educational level ranged from elementary school to advanced graduate degrees with the highest group having some high school (31.1%).

Leadership Questionnaire Responses

The Conger-Kanungo Scale

In the questionnaire, Fr. Paul was perceived as a leader who could recognize the abilities and skills of other members of the organization as well as being able to acknowledge their limitations and was seen as having a visionary approach and the ability to urge others to follow his suggestions. He was acknowledged as being able to see clearly ahead so as to make future plans that facilitate achievement of organizational objectives. He was further identified as a person who takes high risks and who makes personal sacrifices for the sake of the organization.

As shown in Table 1, of the Leadership Questionnaire Responses, Part I, the highest average score relating to Fr. Paul as most highly characteristic was their perception of him as an exciting public speaker (5.83). The next two highest scores respectively were "Shows sensitivity for the needs and feelings of other members in the organization" (5.76) and "In pursuing organizational objectives, engages in activities involving considerable self-sacrifice" (5.75). These are closely followed by "Inspirational, able to motivate by articulating effectively the importance of what organizational members are doing" (5.71), "Often expresses personal concern for the needs and feelings of other members of the organization" (5.59), "Readily recognizes barriers/forces within the organization that may block or hinder achievement of his/her goals" (5.58). The next two items yielded an average of 5.57 and 5.56 respectively, "Appears to be a skillful performer when presenting to a group," "Provides inspiring strategic and organizational goals."

The lowest score indicating the least charismatic feature of Fr. Paul, with an average of 2.97 "Tries to change 'The System' by creating a new system" shows a discrepancy which is probably due to the manner in which the respondents interpreted the word "System." Did it mean the "Brentwood System" or the "Societal System"? The next three lowest mean scores were "Advocates following non-risky well-established courses of action to achieve organizational goals" (3.95), "Engages in unconventional behaviour to achieve organizational goals" (3.93), "Often acts as a reformer to change the values and goals of the organization" (3.92).

A Comparison: Business vs. Human Service

The importance of these high average scores can be seen more clearly by a comparison to the scores obtained in the results from the business trials. The Conger-Kanungo scale was administered to four business establishments to measure the charismatic leadership of their managers. When the scores of all 29 items were added together (summated) and averaged for all respondents, the summated average score for Father Paul was 145.87 while the summated score for the business organizations was only 123.81, meaning that the respondents saw him as more charismatic than those of the other studies saw their counterparts.

	TABLE 1
Leadership Questionnaire Response	

		Average Score
19.	Exciting public speaker.	5.83
7.	Shows sensitivity for the needs and feelings of other members in the organization.	5.76
9.	In pursuing organizational objectives, engages in activities involving considerable self-sacrifice.	5.75
16.	Inspirational, able to motivate by articulating effectively the importance of what organizational members are doing.	5.71
20.	Often expresses personal concern for the needs and feelings of other members of the organization.	5.59
4.	Readily recognizes barriers/forces within the organization that may block or hinder achievement of his/her goals.	5.58
25.	Appears to be a skillful performer when presenting to a group.	5.57
13.	Provides inspiring strategic and organizational goals.	5.56
1.	Influences others by developing mutual liking and respect.	5.53
23.	Recognizes the abilities and skills of other members in the organization.	5.52
15.	Takes high personal risks for the sake of the organization.	5.51
26.	Has vision, often brings up ideas about possibilities for the future.	5.51
28.	Recognizes the limitations of other members in the organization.	5.50
17.	Often urges others to follow his/her suggestions.	5.42
27.	Readily recognizes new environmental opportunities (favorable physical and social conditions) that may facilitate achievement of organizational objectives.	5.38
14.	Readily recognizes constraints in the organization's social and cultural environment (cultural norms, lack of grass roots support, etc.) that may stand in the way of achieving organizational objectives.	5.36
6.	Entrepreneurial; seizes new opportunities to achieve goals.	5.32
24.	Often incurs high personal costs for the good of the organization.	5.26
10.	Readily recognizes constraints in the physical environment (technological limitations, lack of resources, etc.) that may stand in the way of achieving organizational objectives.	5.21

		Average Score
	TABLE 1 continued	
	Leadership Questionnaire Response	
18.	Consistently generates new ideas for the future of the organization.	5.16
2.	Advocates future goals that are not very different from present goals of the organization.	5.11
29.	In pursuing organizational objectives engages in activities involving considerable personal risk.	4.84
21.	Tries to maintain the status quo or the normal way of doing things.	4.65
22.	Often exhibits very unique behavior that surprises other members of the organization.	4.64
8.	Uses non-traditional means to achieve organizational goals.	4.14
11.	Advocates following non-risky well-established courses of action to achieve organizational goals.	3.95
5.	Engages in unconventional behavior to achieve organizational goals.	3.93
12.	Often acts as a reformer to change the values and goals of the organization.	3.92
3.	Tries to change "The System" by creating a new system.	2.97

Conclusion

The results of the study strongly indicate that Fr. Paul Charbonneau is perceived as a charismatic leader by his followers. It also reveals a consistency in the findings of this study when compared to the results of the Conger-Kanungo study in that it fits within the deviation indicated by Conger and Kanungo.

CHAPTER 9

Epilogue and Future Plans[1]

I have attempted to highlight the positive dimensions which render Brentwood one of the leading recovery facilities in Canada. It will be left to others to explore more closely the areas which require further thought and systematic investigation. My purpose was to present the good which is being done there and to have those involved in Brentwood be able to say: "Yes, this is an accurate and conscientious reflection of the Brentwood model."

The facts, thoughts, ideas and expressions in this work are the results of a combined effort of those associated with Brentwood. They reflect my own experience and that of countless others who have contributed their own input in numerous ways. This study has been a product of shared communication of what Brentwood actually entails.

Authority

Fr. Paul is imbued with a cosmic sense of God and of nature. He knew the healing strength of nature and the saving power of God's love which is manifested *in and through other people*. In fact, he sees these two forces as one and attempts to instill in his followers the simplicity of the message of "good news" which is available for anyone who has the willingness to respond to the love and respect offered them. He sees his task as bringing people to a realization of the importance of their oneness with God and with nature in and through other people. He also sees that the recovery process calls for an allegiance to a source of *authority* outside of themselves since alcoholics lack totally an inner sense of discipline and their own authority and must, therefore, follow someone else's authority until such time as they are able to act responsibly on their own. One might say that alcoholics borrow Fr. Paul's will until such time as they are able to exercise fittingly their own free will.

---

1.   The author is indebted to Jean Vanier and Matthew Fox for their inspiration and insight since it is from them that the author has modelled the organization and structure of this concluding chapter.

175

It is through this process of recovery that they can be one with God and nature, with family and friends and take their responsible place in the world of work.

There is no desire on the part of Fr. Paul to take away anyone's right to make their own decisions or anyone's responsibility to do so. This right and power was simply something which they never had or something which they never exercised properly. The decision-making ability of alcoholics has invariably become cloudy and their allegiance to authority has gone adrift. According to Hatterer (1980) there has been a period of maladaptation to authority:

> The addictive process can continue to be rooted in an inability to deal with authority or to rebel satisfactorily and establish status and self-respect among family and peers during adolescence. Later there are difficulties in larger social arenas such as advanced education, jobs, and the law; because of increasing alienation, these become amplified as the process progresses. The inability to accept control or to exercise sufficient controls leads to dysfunction and attempts at psychic repair by destructive domination or excessive submission. Inability to tolerate any imbalances in control, dominance, and submission continually fuels addictiveness. (p. 20)

Fr. Paul has never attempted to make people overly dependent, but only to provide them with the means by which they can come to their own mature sense of *interdependence, freedom* and the ability to take *responsibility* for their own *thoughts, decisions* and *actions.* He actually rejoices when his followers are no longer acting like children but are able to act as mature adults with their own inner sense of accountability. One can parallel Brentwood to a family, where a child has to learn the basics of living before she can go on her own. Just as a father has to discipline a child who is misbehaving, is not following the rules and who is disrupting the family equilibrium, so too Fr. Paul, because of his consideration for the rest of the family members, has to have a certain degree of authority and legitimate control in order for Brentwood to run smoothly. It would be irresponsible on his part to allow residents to continue acting as immature and irresponsible children unless he were taking the practical steps to bring them to maturity. He longs for the day when he can see each of his followers not as dependents who rely solely on him but as grown adults who are *his friends* and who can make their own responsible decisions. He rejoices much like a father who sees that his own child is ready to *go it* on her own and be meaningfully engaged with other people.

What renders the Brentwood experience so strong and vibrant for the residents is the total commitment of Fr. Paul and the staff he has trained to being present to and honest with them. He searches the truth in his own heart, continues to discover what God and nature means to him and is able to communicate this message in such an effective manner as to gather a faithful group of followers. They, in turn, respond to this same truth within themselves. With great diligence he spends the time, energy and resources to unfold this inner reality in each and every person whom he encounters. He *takes the time* to enter their world, and patiently listens to their story so as to unravel the elements of the disease which has left them immobile. It is this profound approach that allows him to enter the lives of people and to bring about a beneficial change in their lives and it is this which liberates them to cultivate their own inner resources. He is the channel by which they can be helped to become clear of their distortions and become free to be themselves. He is like a guide on a journey who is there for them until they no longer require him. The intent is that each person strive toward their own maturity and accept the challenge to be their own person.

Alcoholism, Addiction and Substance Abuse

It has been clear from this study that, from its long experience, Brentwood gathers the three elements of alcoholism, addiction and substance abuse under one umbrella concept of "alcoholism." Although the first clientele at Charity House were alcoholic, it was soon apparent to Fr. Paul and the staff that there are many characteristics which are common to all three dimensions. It is for this reason that the word *alcoholic* is still used interchangeably at Brentwood with addict and substance abuser.

Although alcohol consumption is the most visible behaviour for the alcoholic, drugs for the substance abuser and excessive engagement for the addicted individual, the people who come to Brentwood for help are distinctively saddled with problems similar to their alcoholic and substance abusing peers. Brentwood has come to see the underlying cause of the addictive process as a closed heart—a heart which is oblivious to the psychological, emotional, social and spiritual dimensions which permeate a person's life. Each addict is initially enthralled by a "pleasure vacuum" which is self-serving and which fails to respect the rights and integrity of others. Since each addict or alcoholic is so preoccupied in this pleasure vacuum, he or she sees no need to change until such time as problems have reached extreme proportions.

One of the first requirements in helping alcoholics is to enable them to discover what, in their lives, triggers and perpetuates their condition. As Hatterer states:

> To understand addiction and help an addict help himself, one must discover and help him identify (i.e, become conscious of) the specific triggers that spark and perpetuate his addictiveness. They may be depression, isolation, loneliness, boredom, situational life crises (divorce, death of parent, etc.), severe failures (at work, in love, over money), sex and gender dysfunctions, unbearable pressures, stressful competition, fatigue, overwork, excessive exposure to other

addicts (i.e., addictive milieus), psychosis (i.e., the addictive agent is used as self-medication), and so forth. (p. 24)

Brentwood has found that there is a strong narcissistic tendency in most alcoholics. They fail to "own" their integrity and to stand up as mature adults. They forfeit their own uniqueness because of a distorted perception of themselves. For some the deception is grandiose and for others it is diminutive as they consistently put themselves down. Their lives resemble an empty reservoir which is devoid of feeling or self-worth. Their constant goal is self-indulgence at the expense of others. Alexander Lowen defines the narcissist in much the same way as Brentwood looks upon the alcoholic as "a person who is preoccupied with him or herself to the exclusion of everyone else" (1985, p. 6).

When blindness to emotions is more important than being loved, when being closed is more meaningful than a "shared community," when fantasy is more significant than living in the here-and-now, and when stagnation and isolation are more important than growth, aliveness and celebration with others, we find a person who is, in the Brentwood perspective, "alcoholic": a person addicted to either people, places or things which render her life senseless, ineffective and clearly dysfunctional. In effect, a false stanchion or decadent prop is used to diffuse the fear of love and encounter. According to Hatterer (1980), individuals in the addictive process seek dysfunctional gratification in various choice areas which at first are experienced as pleasurable and are used to deal with conflict but which eventually remain unresolved:

A person should be considered addicted when an overpowering, repetitive, excessive need exists for some substance, object, feeling, act, milieu, or personal interaction at any cost, along with a denial of the destructive consequences to one's physical, emotional, and social well-being and, in some instances, to economic survival. In true addiction there is almost always excessive use of pleasurable activities to cope with manageable internal conflict, pressure, stress, and confrontation. The person has little tolerance for frustration and cannot balance pleasure and pain, work and play. There is also impaired self-esteem, and conflicts about dependence, control, discipline, passivity, and aggressiveness. (p. 17)

Trust and Treatment

Brentwood has found that, of themselves, alcoholics are not able to emerge from their sickness because they do not trust anyone, and without trust there is no genuine encounter. The alcoholic has no strong foundation because all goals are destructively enmeshed in a misplaced obsession for lust, inordinate power, control, sexual prowess, workaholism, seduction, family dysfunction and pseudo relationships. The alcoholic/addictive-type personalities refuse to grow, and live in fantasy as opposed to reality. They are oblivious to the world around them because of their narrow preoccupation with their limited self. By living a life which is out of touch with God and other people they are in constant turmoil and confusion. Alcoholic and addictive individuals who work at the Brentwood program find themselves in a *"spiritual rift"* and must move into truth from falsehood, into light from darkness, into growth from stagnation and into life from death. Their thoughts, feelings and behaviours are set on destruction and death, because their mind is sluggish and lethargic, their heart is lifeless and their body is spent and anesthetized. All of these symptoms, of course, point to the underlying disease of narcissism.

Narcissists are in accord with the findings of Lowen about narcissistic people who, having deadened themselves, are anesthetized to pain and this is displayed in their insensitivity to others:

> They can be ruthless, exploitative, sadistic, or destructive to another person because they are insensitive to the other's suffering or feeling. This insensitivity derives from an insensitivity to one's own feelings. Empathy, the ability to sense other people's moods or feelings, is a function of resonance. (p. 49)

The experiences of Brentwood also points to the same cause and perpetuation of addictions as found by Hatterer who states:

> Authors who have researched and written about the addictions inevitably focus on the importance of narcissistic imbalance as a common cause and perpetuation of the addictive process. Because the addict has suffered from early disruption, damage, or trauma to the development and establishment of his ego and superego and to his nurturance and dependency need, he must incur narcissistic disturbances. These disturbances are reflected in his relationships with others and attitudes toward himself. Imbalances occur in his ability to perceive himself accurately or to deal equitably with others. (p. 31)

Fr. Paul set out to fashion a people with a collective consciousness, who would break the bonds of narcissism by being primarily "other-centered" and "community-oriented." He engendered in them an abiding "in-faith-community" with caring and sharing at its very roots.

A Healing Community

Brentwood was created because Fr. Paul had a prophetic vision of the way life ought to be lived and of the need to establish a healing community where spiritual transformation could occur. He had a dream of a better world for those afflicted with the disease of alcoholism, addiction and substance abuse akin to the renewed spiritual cosmology which Matthew Fox explains:

✳   Is it possible that the real cause of the drug, alcohol, and entertainment addictions haunting our society is not so much the "drug lords" of other societies but the cosmic loneliness haunting our own? Perhaps alcohol is a liquid cosmology and drugs are a fast-fix cosmology for people lacking a true one. (1983, p. 2)   ✳

Fr. Paul has instilled in his followers a lasting sense of hope and fulfillment in their lives through the existence of a meaningful community where the alcoholic could experience the essential aspects of love and caring. It is this inmost setting which must be created in order to make life hopeful and joyful for them. They need to know that they are worthwhile and valuable as human beings and that they do indeed have a valid contribution to make. Such a welcoming warmth and affection is necessary as the starting point of their journey into maturity and aliveness. How can anyone *act* as a brother or sister if they have never experienced what it is actually like to *be* a brother or sister? How can a mother *be* a mother without first having had the experience of *having been* a daughter? The same applies to being a dad.

Jean Vanier (1985) captures the spirit which personifies Brentwood when he comments on how community life with its sense of celebration and aliveness, its sharing and its love, gives a sense of belonging and security. He indicates how a spiritual community needs to be a home, a place of tenderness and security:

✳   The first thing that someone with a handicap, *and indeed everyone*, needs is to feel at home. It is the sense of belonging to a group and of finding one's place there. Someone who feels a burden on others, or feels welcomed only out of pity, cannot feel at home.... Those who find a community where they feel truly at home, where they are loved and respected and where they have a special role and responsibility, will progress in the integration of their beings.... Community relationships resemble the relationship which exists between brothers and sisters in a family. This is a simple, deep relationship, full of affection, where each complements the other. (p. 80, 81)   ✳

Fr. Paul knew suffering because he had experienced so much sorrow and desolation in his own growing years. The Brentwood story enkindles in the hearts of people a renewed fervor for the quality of life and awakens them with the hope of achieving new vistas which strengthen and fortify the way in which they reach out to one another. As people practice the principles of the program, they become more whole and as a consequence, more a "prism" of God's love to each other. The ripple effect produced draws people into a creative mosaic where authentic bonding is given its form, shape and texture. Brentwood gives birth to patience, understanding and compassion towards one another and is a living witness of its immense capacity to assuage the pain and suffering of the most wounded of people. The Brentwood process is able to lift people toward their most noble calling and to fulfill their yet unrealized potential.

Through the healing power of people being present to one another, a redemptive quality of caring and compassion directs them to an increased level of self-confidence and other-directedness. The call for compassion is vividly recalled in a passage from St. Paul in his letter to the Philippians:

> Complete my joy by being of the same mind, having the same love, being in full accord and of one mind. Do nothing from selfishness or conceit.... Let each of you look to the interests of others. (2:2–5)

This insightful passage very much reflects the unifying principle of Brentwood which calls people to do "God's will" as opposed to "self-will." Fr. Paul's grasp of the immense value of human life emerged from his deep understanding and his penetrating compassion for the suffering of others. He seems to have an almost infinite capacity to reach into the heart of afflicted people and to draw forth a rich source of life and renewal. What Henry Nouwen remarkably observed of Jean Vanier applies also to Fr. Paul: "He is a pastor who gently and patiently points to the presence of God where we least expect it" (Vanier, 1985, p. iv). He makes his followers aware that by being able to accept the relative and imperfect love of people that they can discover the absolute and infinite love of God. Fr. Paul is conscious of the fact that those who are afflicted with the wounds of alcoholism, addiction and substance abuse are pleading predominantly for a deep sense of love and belonging in their lives. He knows they are craving *spiritual affection* and *spiritual communion* with others. He offers the promise of a new day and a new life.

A Break from Tradition

Fr. Paul provides a symbiotic learning environment at Brentwood which, in the words of Henry Nouwan (1971), is a shift from teaching as a violent process to teaching as a redemptive activity. A redemptive activity as Nouwan sees it calls for a mutual sense of acceptance where teachers allow themselves to be students and students to be teachers to one another. In Fr. Paul's own words: "I patiently listened to these people for countless years before I intervened in terms of direction or advice-giving. I watched and observed what the recovering alcoholic did and I followed the example which seemed to work so effectively with them. I became a student again so that I could learn from them."

The redemptive teacher-learner approach is a shift from education as *competitive, unilateral, and alienating to it being evocative, bilateral and actualizing.* There is no competition among the residents to succeed at the expense of others on program. As opposed to being unilateral, there is ample room for residents to learn from each other and to nurture and sustain one another. Brentwood is far from being alienating since people are actively invested in acting out their issues in such a way that provides a new meaning and perspective to their lives. Fr. Paul's activities are evocative to the extent that he always shares his own unique story and carefully explains how he came to grips with the unresolved issues in his own life. He openly shares his own strengths and weaknesses which makes residents feel that they are integrally related to him. The Brentwood process is bilateral to the extent that Fr. Paul has always remained open to learning from those on program and from the fellowship. In fact, the Brentwood model prepares residents to actualize their potential by a deep investment in the here-and-now. It is at Brentwood that the residents learn from repeated example how the quality of *authentic spiritual community* is actually experienced.

It was Fr. Paul's ability to break with tradition and discard outdated beliefs which freed him to embark upon a novel approach to recovery. He reaches beyond the suffering of alcoholics and he raises them up to a dignity and self-worth which they have never before experienced, and by having people enter the depth of their pain and suffering, he is able to help them transform their lives to a level which they never conceived of as possible before this time. Brentwood teaches people a true sense of interdependence and of the integral need people have for one another. As a result people make conscious choices to *be there* for others.

Fr. Paul learned of the need of the alcoholic for authentic relationships by attending sensitively to their suffering much as Jean Vanier (1985) did with the mentally handicapped:

> ✳   In welcoming and listening to Raphael and Philippe, and so many others who had been put aside, I let myself be carried into an unknown world. I discovered the depth of their sufferings, the cry within them for authentic relationships, as well as the joy of living together [in community]. (p. 2)   ✳

Fr. Paul was cognizant of the fact that in order to deal with the plight of alcoholics, he had to be able to see within their pain and their anguish a link with the critical issues relevant to the disease of alcoholism and addiction. He did not rush foolhardily into this endeavor but painstakingly took the time and patience to invest himself wholeheartedly. It has been his unwavering persistence which has seen him through the most difficult times. He was able to penetrate with both a microscopic and a telescopic view their immense suffering and in the process was able to carefully tend to them at the core of their humanness. Like Hatterer, he has been able to see how each addict or alcoholic:

> ...can shift from arrogance to indifference, from the pain of total self-negation to the pleasure of complete self-absorption, from ag-

gressive self-preoccupation to pseudo-compliance, solicitude, and a passivity that camouflages his excessive needs. (p. 32)

It is important for the alcoholic to move from darkness to light, from desperation to hope and from weakness to strength. In essence, Brentwood offers a shift from negative and damaging attitudes and behaviours to positive and healthful ways; from self-flagellation to communal healing; from inordinate selfishness to genuine other-centeredness; from a false sense of power to an authentic sense of caring; from a false sense of religion to a renewed spirituality; from acting as a mirror of imperfections and fault-finding to a beaming prism of God's love; from holding on to old habits of dishonesty and deceit to embracing new levels of truth and honesty; from imprisonment and isolation to liberation; and from futile guilt-tripping in a needless preoccupation with the past to being fully alive in the present and engaged in the "here-and-now."

Fr. Paul has been able to heal a large number of people. He is able to awaken in their hearts a sense of getting in touch with their inner being and of reclaiming their own human nature in a way which raises them up in dignity to an authentic celebration of aliveness. Perhaps one of his most incredible features is his cosmic sense of suffering and his innate knowledge that people need to be redeemed and nurtured in their suffering. He sees pain and suffering as an inevitable aspect of life—not something to run away from as into booze, drugs or addiction, but something to be reconciled with. He sensitively understands that people have to embrace their pain and own it as their own if any true and authentic growth is going to unfold in their lives. Once people can acknowledge the pain in themselves, they are able to enter into the joy. Failing to risk the pain, they invariably cannot experience the surge of maturity and emancipation. Analogous to a seed being planted, unless it dies by being placed in the soil it cannot become a flower, nor can a caterpillar become a butterfly unless it spins itself into a cocoon. So too, people have to die to "self-will" and allow "God's will" to reign *in, with, for, through* and *from* other people. Hope stems from the reality of doing what is natural to ourselves as human beings.

In addition to moving from a paradigm shift, Brentwood provides an opportunity for story-telling. By hearing themselves out loud, the residents and alumni have a chance to deal directly with the enemy that lurks deep within. They no longer have to hold on to their mistaken projections but they can be free to live *for, with* and *through* other people. They can now make a responsible commitment to "be there" for others in the richest sense of the term. By this type of surrender, the person can venture into the unknown with a renewed confidence and self-worth. There is no longer a need to hide behind a bottle, a substance, a relationship or to play games at their own and everyone else's expense.

A Woundedness Healed

Brentwood fosters a creative spirit within each individual by restoring their confidence, their self-worth and their self-esteem to the point where they are able to give credence to new possibilities and new experiences in their lives. In their disease, they have been plagued with aggression, despair and despondency, all barriers to true creativity. They exhausted their own creative resources and they deprived others of their right and need to be creative and, consequently, unique. Brentwood has often made reference to a *closed heart*. Jean Vanier (1985) sees the closed and wounded heart as concealed and obscured, disclosing itself through dread, uncertainty, discouragement, chaos, illusion and withdrawal from reality: "Above all, it is manifested by a broken image of self, a profound guilt and a refusal of life" (p. 11). In speaking of the division which rests in the heart of wounded people and of the defense system which protects their vulnerability he maintains:

> *   This deep wound of the heart is the source of their bizarre behaviour, whether aggressive or depressive. Not having been recognized as true human beings, capable of growth, they are unable even to begin forming a true relationship with another. Having always been considered by others as an object, they will consider others as objects; they cannot imagine that they are capable of giving life and happiness to another. In order to live they must make the transition from a negative self-image to a positive one, from a feeling of being without value to a feeling of being valued. Who will help them make this transition? (p. 17)   *

The basic problem with alcoholics has been a refusal to acknowledge the pain, grief and anger in their lives. Fox (1983) quotes Macy who advises:

> *   Experience the pain. Let us not fear its impact on ourselves or others. We will not shatter, for we are not objects that can break. Nor will we get stuck in this pain for it is dynamic, it flows through us. Drop our defenses, let us stay present to its flow, express it—in words, movements and sounds. (p. 153)   *

A Dream in Touch with Reality

Some people with no prior experience of Brentwood may mistakenly feel that Fr. Paul prevents people from having a "dream." This is much to the contrary. Alcoholics have for so long lived in fantasy, isolation and despair and have severed themselves from any contact with the real world. They entertained false dreams which had no connection with reality. What Fr. Paul has attempted to do is to have the alcoholic live in reality so that he or she could have dreams which are worthy of human achievement and of playful exploration. Dreams help to bring out the healthy "child" in us all. Jean Vanier (1985) explains how dreams can either open someone to reality and love or how they can cut someone off from reality:

* A dream is a sign of health; it shows that life is stronger than death. To have no dream can be hell, a sign of utter despair. The dream, like psychosis, is a refusal of death; it is a way of reacting to inner pain. It is important therefore not to shatter the dream too quickly on the grounds of putting people in touch with reality, a reality which may be unbearable for them. When a physical handicap (or psychological handicap, like addiction) constantly reminds one of one's powerlessness, reality can be unbearable. At the same time, to allow a person to be buried in the world of dreams is in some way to confirm them in isolation. This is the tragedy of those who take drugs: even when they are together, each one is terribly alone, imprisoned in a dream. (p. 89) *

Brentwood provides an opportunity for people who never received any authentic sense of love to become grounded in the more intense meaning of life and to grasp a deeper appreciation of what it means to be loved and cared for. People become responsible for one another through a genuine spirit of community. Each person feels a sense of belonging and a renewed sense of purpose. This type of bond provides for healthy dreams without the illusions which are a mere departure from reality and which only serve as an escape from the emptiness of a closed and broken heart. People serve as powerful role models because as each one strives to remain true to developing their own potential, they help others to achieve theirs. This mutual sense of helping one another has a very strong ripple effect which "rubs off" throughout the whole fellowship and creates a cohesive union and commitment to one another. As Jean Vanier explains, people come to realize that they are loved with tenderness and care and that they are capable of loving, of working, of serving and of living with others as sisters and brothers. Through an awareness of their humanity, they uncover the richness of *giving* and *receiving*. As Jean Vanier (1985) explains:

* This, in fact, is one of the goals of community and education: it is also a family where each one can live authentic and liberating relationships...like a family, its members are linked to one another in mutual trust and respect, and by a deep sense of belonging. This is expressed in the spontaneity and animation of real celebrations and festivities. A family has one soul and one heart.... Community implies a real fellowship where people truly listen to one another in love. (p. 99) *

Marriage and Family
Objection is often given by people who feel that Fr. Paul is in no position to speak with authority on matters pertaining to marriage,

family and sexuality by virtue of the fact that he has never been married himself and has no children of his own. It must be remembered that Fr. Paul came from a human family and was exposed to the day-to-day events of family life. He encountered familial experiences in his seminary years, he lived with fellow priests and he continually encountered a multitude of family dynamics in his work as a parish priest. In addition, he has listened attentively to the pain of countless people who have come to him over the years repeating stories which have a common thread and a customary theme. Fr. Paul has created his own sense of family where he has very much been "father" to a multitude of people. Experience shows that he has been able to gather an immense "practice wisdom" which would surpass the ordinary parent by virtue of the hours of time and commitment he has so generously given to those who have become part of the Brentwood family. As Jean Vanier (1985) would say, he knows how to create community—community which stems from integrity, honesty, love, forgiveness, covenant and celebration:

> ✳   Sometimes people say that the Church and religious leaders have no right to speak of genital sexuality because many of them are celibates. Experience shows me that priests often have a great understanding of the human heart through the thousands and thousands of confidences given to them in individual confessions or through spiritual direction. Many of them have more knowledge of the demands and difficulties of love than psychologists. They have received these confidences in a deeper light than psychology, in light of the intimate and spiritual consciences of people. (p. 105)   ✳

The celibate person who has harnessed his sexual energy can stand as a beacon to those who have not come to grips with their own sexual issues and can be a living witness to the oppressed of how to deal with obscurity. As Matthew Fox contends, a celibate can stand in solidarity and compassion with people who feel deprived in their sexuality for he or she also represents a sexual minority: "People ought to acknowledge a well-kept secret in our society—much celibacy is being practiced by single persons and others every day. Celibacy is not restricted to the formally vowed individual" (p. 209). Fox contends that the celibate has frequently been cast in the wilderness to find a solution for the cosmic loneliness of our times. Fr. Paul's method and approach is an antidote to this deep-seated isolation and forsaken desperation.

Setting the Downtrodden Free

Fox (1983) quotes Kabir who defines a holy person as "one who is aware of others' suffering." (p. 234). Fr. Paul has extended himself in compassion and gentleness into the heart of suffering people. In a rather prophetic sense, Fr. Paul's mission can be seen more clearly when one examines the people to whom he ministers. He is not chiefly occupied with the intellectual, the well-to-do or the elitist of society but he attends mostly to the weak, the outcast, the downtrodden, the poor, the afflicted and those who are not recognized in the community. The outcasts are precious to his eyes and he painstakingly nurtures them to health—from narcissism to maturity. Over the years, he has invited people from all walks of life to enter the process of recovery so that healing can occur in their lives. Fr. Paul proclaims the "good tidings" that forgiveness and love are possible when people open up their minds and hearts to one another.

He has reached out to those ridiculed and rejected by society and to those who are poor and in need. Inasmuch as the call of religion is a call to compassion, it can be said that Brentwood is a "religious community" to the extent that it is loving and sensitive to those it invites into its care. It reaches out to those who would otherwise be perceived as mere numbers, as faceless people in a crowd with no say in their own destiny. Brentwood makes them lovable again and embraces them as part of the human family. The Brentwood experience is open to those who want to mend their wounds and who want to celebrate life again, the way it was originally meant to be—the way nature intended.

Brentwood teaches people how to enter their individual struggles, how to own them as their own and then how to discard them once they realize that they no longer need the negative aspects which bog them down and which diminish their energy level and life-force.

Brentwood is an experience which effectively blends both the paternal and the maternal components which are so complementary in the life of an individual. This combined thrust has it roots in the person of Fr. Paul who in the wisdom of his own experience can be not only gentle and directive, but also compassionate and understanding. He is also able to exercise an untiring sense of empathy and gentleness towards those who suffer so deeply. It is this combination of head and heart which renders Brentwood so dramatically effective. It is for this reason that residents say: "Everything he says is so true to life and applies exactly to my own circumstances. It sounds like he is speaking directly to me." This is understandable because Fr. Paul speaks a universal language of the heart. He combines the *"darkness of the soul"* which has entrapped people to a living *"hell on earth"* with *"an ecstacy of the spirit"* which renders people *"fully alive"*. He knew he was on a course that was true to the message of the gospel—to bring the good news that people are loved in and through one another. The momentum and impetus created has provided for a nurturing environment which has been a rich "soilbed" for a fruitful "spiritual awakening" for those who need to transform their lives from "darkness" to "light."

Without contradiction, Fr. Paul has always been a "practical idealist." He knows what people are capable of becoming but is prudent enough not to expect or to demand perfection from them. Fr. Paul never hid behind the "rostrum of intelligentsia" to mask or diminish his message of love and good-will. In his talks Fr. Paul is able to provide strategic links which draw people together. He gives people a thirst for community and instills within them a deep yearning of the heart to be united in a common bond of trust, hope and love. What makes Brentwood so powerful is the fact that as a "faith-community" it celebrates pain and suffering and openly acknowledges the need people have for one another. It is the very process of entering into their anguish and despair which allows them an opportunity to recognize the dialectic between sadness and joy, love and hate, peace and anger, darkness and light, weakness and strength, death and life. By embracing both sides of the human condition, people are brought to a fullness of life which makes celebration and rejoicing possible.

At Brentwood there is no pristine facade to hide the hurt, guilt and remorse but a candid disclosure of the fears and anxieties which have led people to such immense suffering and alienation from others. It is being "part of" and the very "entering in" process which allows people to accept the positive and the negative, the good and the bad in their lives. Knowing that they are loved as they are gives them the courage and strength to sustain and survive any conceivable ordeal or obstacle.

Jean Vanier (1985) explains that the story of our broken lives is a "story of woundedness." By listening to their own pain the people of Brentwood become more attuned to the impassioned cry of others who are scarred and wounded. With the tremendous surge of energy which envelops them, they are filled with peace and gratitude—a "thank you" for the gifts received and a sense of wanting to return the same to others in the same measure in which is was meted out to them. Again, the ripple effect of love—caring and sharing, giving and receiving is recycled into the mainstream of everyday life. It is not only a power which sustains them but it is a life-giving force which nurtures the very soul of their being. They become integrally one with God, nature and other people. In turn, they brave the elements with a confidence and rigor which sometimes, by ordinary standards, defies human understanding.

The Authenticity of Community

Brentwood stands as a guidepost for a new sense of commitment and a new sense of direction in terms of the expansion of human communities because of its unique approach to the human condition. The universal principles which it applies make it a practical model for those afflicted with diverse types of addictions and with various kinds of spiritual ailments.

Brentwood offers a spirituality for the "here and now" where people can fully embrace the richness of the present through the celebration of togetherness whether in the "one-on-ones," in the shared sense of "family" or in the engagement of "community." It takes an indomitable courage to let go of the past and to relinquish one's needless preoccupation with the future. Alcoholics and addicts have suffered severe trauma in their *past* relationships, are unable to deal effectively in the *present* in their interactions with others and fear any viable prospects for the *future*. In their fear or in their lack of control and in their increased negativity, they gravitate to immediate satisfaction in areas which are progressively detrimental and increasingly deadly. Brentwood concentrates on the "ever-present-now" where life can be lived to its optimum. Being fully attuned to the present ushers within people a resurgent sense of responsibility and accountability to one another.

Brentwood and the Future

Fr. Paul is getting to the age where he will have to retire and the question is often asked: "Who will replace him?" This is no easy feat. Though anyone can usually be replaced, this is not so readily the case with him. Some fail to the see the uniqueness of Fr. Paul's solitary contribution and dedication. One has to examine Brentwood's overall structure. He created this program with the help of others and it simply cannot be duplicated. He maintains that there will always be strong alumni there to carry the torch. It is important that Brentwood go on in such a way that its spirit prevails. Any recovery home can go on indefinitely but it is essential to perpetuate those precise elements which make Brentwood unique and which give it its vigor and vitality. It is important that the philosophy not be lost—the heart and pulse of what makes Brentwood, *Brentwood*.

Fr. Paul will ensure that the spiritual aspect of Brentwood will not be lost by falling into the wrong hands. Efforts are being made to ensure that the right people fill the appropriate positions. Though it is not possible to find one person who can have the kind of substance, ability, vision, authority and driving force which has personified Fr. Paul, he feels that his source of support will come from a group of people, not just one individual, who will bring different gifts and dimensions into the various areas. There are a great deal of dedicated alumni who will be able to carry the torch though they understandably will not have the same sense of mission and devotion which characterized Fr. Paul.

Brentwood has been a blessing not only to the alcoholic but also to Fr. Paul. His charisma would not have come out as poignantly had it not been for this unique discovery of healing the alcoholic. It is this which gives him the strength where he is on the go constantly and he never gives up his undaunting spirit. He never tires. If he did not have this intense feeling for the alcoholic it would not as readily be there. He has an inexhaustible reservoir. It would be almost impossible to find another person with this type of capacity to give to Brentwood.

The key plan for the future basically has to centre on the fact that Fr. Paul is not going to be at the head. Steps have been taken in the last four years, and continue to be taken before his eventual retirement. Having the groups functioning effectively at Brentwood is one of the steps which have been initiated where group leaders have been chosen and trained to carry on the bulk of the work in terms of the process of "recovery therapy." The whole Brentwood operation will function around the group leaders and others who have been given different responsibilities. Efforts are being made to ensure that there will be sufficient counsellors in addition to the group leaders to carry on the tasks in which Fr. Paul has been involved.

Further Research

Brentwood's potential involvement in the area of systematic and scholarly research is very promising. When people benefit from a place such as Brentwood, it is inescapable that they want to tell their friends about it. A potential research project could include a study of all the alumni, especially those in distant places, to discover what they are now doing in terms of the quality of their lives. What is their present attitude? Do they still have the Brentwood thinking which has been ingrained in them? This could be readily done by taking the mailing list and by sending out a questionnaire in which the respondents could share their own experience before and after Brentwood. What have their lives been like since they have graduated from Brentwood? What people have they touched? What people have they been instrumental in getting help for with their alcohol, drug or addictive issues?

Future studies will quite assuredly be done, especially with the initiation of a full-time clinical psychologist on staff. The area of research will most likely be dealt with more vigorously and more intensely. Research will be conducted in the role Brentwood continues to play in the whole area of alcoholism, addiction and substance abuse.

Fr. Paul—A Guiding Light

People are not just *in and out* of Brentwood but are provided with a careful follow-up. This way the alumni are not lost in terms of the extension of their program. They are given continued support and direction because there is someone there to say: "This is how it is done." Jim Ryan explains:

✳   I have known several priests in my lifetime and I have seen good priests but I have never met a priest of Fr. Paul's calibre. What it boils down to is his passionate concern for his fellowman. The fact that he is a priest enhances this because he has had the spiritual background and the spiritual breakthrough in his own life. He wanted to be a man for all people. He had a clear and distinct insight into the difference between *spirituality* and *religiosity*. To me, he had a better sense of it than his teachers had. Most alcoholics would be turned off by a narrow sense of religion, whereas he received a better following through the authenticity of his message. Any other way simply would not have worked. Otherwise, he would have been all over the place and more frustrated than ever.   ✳

There are so many different ideas and approaches to alcoholism. Some happen to capture the imagination of people and are tried, others fail dramatically. It happens that Fr. Paul with an almost charismatic vision has been able to capture the creativity and imagination of his followers with relative success. He has capably constructed a viable alternative to alcoholism, addiction and drug dependence. Fr. Paul does not put himself up on a pedestal to be idolized. He is a person of humble origin who lives a rather modest lifestyle. He sees himself more as a *servant* than as a *leader*. Though a good number of his followers have ascribed the designation of charismatic to him he personally does not attribute this label to himself. Fr. Paul would likely say: "The whole perception of charisma is more in the eyes of the beholder." A person cannot be charismatic unless he or she has followers who ascribe that quality to such a leader. My own tendency is to believe that he does have remarkable characteristics of leadership and an awesome ability to understand and guide the lives of those suffering from alcoholism, addiction and substance abuse.

Since love and respect were given freely they are also dispensed freely at Brentwood. Now the followers are able to carry his message. When Fr. Paul is gone, Brentwood will be able to rely on the depth and wealth of the alumni. They will be able to bear the torch since the spirit of Brentwood now lives within each follower who practices its principles. Now they can increase and multiply, like a ripple effect, the living spirit of Brentwood by touching the lives and hearts of other people. By honestly living the truth within themselves they will actively pass it on to others through their living example.

Perhaps Brentwood's greatest legacy is its ability to engender in people a hope which goes beyond human psychology and which transforms the mundane things of life. Its followers are able to celebrate an extraordinary quality of life with an intensity and a communal wholeness which has to be seen and experienced in order to be properly grasped. At Brentwood there is an immense source of energy which vibrantly resounds in the hearts of people and which is gracefully extended to others. As one staff member remarked: "There is love here and it is here in abundance."

Brentwood provides the foundation for a vibrant life-force where people are truly present *to* and *for* one another. It is not steeped in a dualism which separates head and heart but rather is immersed in a process which integrates and combines both. By seeing the world more holistically, people are able to practice a deepened sense of interdependence and communal wholeness.

Brentwood provides the promise of a rich and abiding community for those who have lost all hope in an era which in so many circles is wrought with doom and desolation. Brentwood is the springboard for a renewed spirituality for all people irrespective of age, creed or color and is a challenge for our time. Brentwood promotes what genuine communities ought to be and offers a new beginning in the lives of wounded people. This is truly Fr. Paul's message: "By entering other people's pain, you can be loving and forgiving and in this you can find your own sense of freedom and happiness." The message of the gospel has always been one of hope and joy and a deep awareness of being loved amidst pain and suffering. Brentwood does this and to this extent truly fulfills the message of good news to all people. Out of joy and gratitude love is born in the heart and this same spirit of peace and love is spread abundantly to other people.

Conclusion

The story of Brentwood is the story of thousands of alcoholics who have been helped to overcome the disease of alcoholism. It is also the story of tens of thousands of the families of alcoholics who have been helped to become free of the demonic forces which totally enslave those whose lives are entangled in the world of the alcoholic. Further, it is the personal story of a man, a priest, who was called and empowered by God and his church to a new understanding of alcoholism and to a new approach to its treatment. And finally it is the story of staff and alumni who have learned from that priest to respect and help alcoholics.

Addiction Research Foundation of Ontario. The Physician's Manual, 1981. In T.E. Bratter & G.G. Forest, G.G. (1985) *Alcoholism and substance abuse: Strategies forclinical intervention.* New York: The Free Press.

Ahlgren, A., Norem, A.A., Hochhauser, M., & Garvin, J., (1982) Antecedents of smoking among preadolescents. *Journal of Drug Education,* 12, 325–340.

Albrecht, T.L. & Adelman, M.B. (Fall, 1984). "Social support and life stress: New directions for communication research". *Human Communication Research,* Vol. 11 No. 1, 3–32.

American Psychiatric Association. *Diagnostic Statistical Manual of Mental Disorders* (DSM-III). 3rd ed. Washington, D.C. American Psychiatric Association, 1980.

Barnes, G.E. (1979) "The alcoholic personality: A reanalysis of the literature". *Journal of Studies on Alcohol,* 1979, 40, 571–634. In T.E. Bratter & G.G. Forest, (1985) *Alcoholism and substance abuse: Strategies for clinical intervention.* New York: The Free Press.

Barnes, G.E. (1980) Characteristics of the clinical alcoholic studies on Alcohol, 41, 894–910. In T.E. Bratter & G.G. Forest, (1985) *Alcoholism and substance abuse: Strategies for clinical intervention.* New York: The Free Press.

Bensman, J., & Givant, M. (1975) "Charisma and modernity: The use and abuse of a concept". *Social Research,* 42, 570–614.

Bratter, T.E., Forest, G.G. (1985) *Alcoholism and substance abuse: Strategiesfor clinical intervention.* New York: The Free Press.

Brownell, A. & Shumaker, S.A. (1984). "Toward a theory of social support: Closing Conceptual Gaps". *Journal of Social Issues,* Vol. 40 No. 4, 1–9.

Bruhn, J.G & Phillips, B.U. (1984). "Measuring social support: A synthesis of current approaches". *Journal of Behavior Medicine,* Vol. 7 No. 2, 151–169.

Burns, J.M. (1978) *Leadership.* New York: Harper & Row.

194 *Sharing the Love that Frees Us*

Carnes, P. (1983) *Out of the shadows: Understanding sexual addiction.* Minneapolis: CompCare Publications.

Caplan, G., Killilea, M. Ed. (1976) *Support systems and mutual help: Multidisciplinary explorations.* New York: Grune & Stratton.

Chein (1969) In T.E. Bratter & G.G. Forest, (1985) *Alcoholism and substance abuse: Strategies for clinical intervention.* New York: The Free Press.

Cicero, T.J. "Alcohol self-administration, tolerance, and withdrawal in humans and animals: Theoretical and methodological issues". (1980) In H. Rigter & J.C. Crabbe (Eds.), *Alcohol Tolerance and Dependence,* New York: Elsevier/North Holland Biomedical Press, In T.E. Bratter & G.G. Forest, (1985) *Alcoholism and substance abuse: Strategies for clinical intervention.* New York: The Free Press.

Clark, B.R. (1972) The organizational saga in higher education. *Administrative Science Quarterly,* 17, 178–184.

Clarke, Bill, S.J. (1974) *Enough room for joy: Jean Vanier's L'Arche: A message for our time.* New York: Paulist Press.

Clinebell Jr., H.J. (1984) *Understanding and counseling the alcoholic: Through Religion and Psychology.* Nashville: Abingdon Press.

Conger, J.A. (1985) *Charismatic leadership in business: An exploratory study.* Unpublished doctoral dissertation, School of Business Administration, Harvard University.

Conger, J.A., & Kanungo., R.N. & Associates. (1988) *Charismatic leadership: The elusive factor in organizational effectiveness.* San Francisco, Calif.: Jossey-Boss.

Conger, J., & Kanungo, R. (1990) *A behavioral measure of charismatic leadership in organizations.* A paper submitted for review to the Organizational Behavior Division of 1990 Academy of Management, San Francisco.

Curran, C.A. (1978). *Understanding: An essential Ingredient in Human Belonging.* Apple River, Ill.: Apple River Press.

Devereux, G. (1955) "Charismatic leadership and crisis". In W. Muensterberger & S. Axelrod (eds.), *Psychoanalysis and the Social Services.* New York: International University Press.

Devin, S. & Gallant, W. *Alcoholism, addiction and Brentwood: Insight for the helping professions.* Unpublished manuscript.

Downton, J.V. (1973) *Rebel leadership: Commitment and charisma in the revolutionary process.* New York: Free Press.

Duncan, D. (1989) *A future operating strategy for Brentwood Recovery Home.* A Major Paper for the Degree of Master of Business Administration. Unpublished manuscript.

Edmonds, S.E. (1989) *The impact of a social support process on alcoholics' communication patterns: A collaborative inquiry.* A Master's Thesis, Windsor, Ont.

Egan, G., (1986) *The skilled helper: A systematic approach to effective helping.* (Third Edition) Monterey, Calif., Brooks\Cole Publishing Company.

DeLeon, G., & Ziegenfuss, J.T. (1986) *Therapeutic communities for addictions: Readings in theory, research and practice.* Springfield, Ill., Charles C. Thomas Pub.

Fox, M. (1983) *The coming of the cosmic Christ.* New York, N.Y.: Harper and Row.

Fromm, E. (1941) *Escape from freedom.* New York: Farrar and Rinehart.

Fulmer, R.H., & Lapidus, L.B. (1980) "A study of professed reasons for beginning and continuing heroin use". *International Journal of Addiction*, 13, 631–645. In T.E. Bratter & G.G. Forest, (1985) *Alcoholism and substance abuse: Strategies for clinical intervention.* New York: The Free Press.

Gallant, W., & Charbonneau, P. *Alcoholism and Brentwood: A spiritual model of recovery.* Burlington, Ont.: Trinity Press. (In Press).

Gilbert, R.M. (1976) "Drug abuse as excessive behavior". *Canadian Psychological Review.* 17, 231–240. In T.E. Bratter & G.G. Forest, (1985) *Alcoholism and substance abuse: Strategies for clinical intervention.* New York: The Free Press.

Goble, F. (1970) *The third force: The Psychology of Abraham Maslow.* New York: Simon & Schuster.

Goodwin, D.W.; Schulsinger, F.; Hermansen, L.; Guze, S.B.; & Wonokur, G. (1973) "Alcohol problems in adoptees raised apart from biological parents". *Archives of General Psychiatry* 28:238–243.

Gorenstein, E.E. (1980) "Relationships of subclinical depression, psychopathy and hysteria to patterns of alcohol consumption and abuse in males and females". In M. Galanter (ed.) *Currents in Alcoholism: Recent Advances in Research and Treatment,* vol. 7. New York: Grune & Stratton.

Hart, L.S., & Stueland, D (1979) "An application of the multidimensional model of alcoholism to program effectiveness. Rehabilitation status and outcome". *Journal of Studies on Alcohol,* 40, 645–655. In T.E. Bratter & G.G. Forest, (1985) *Alcoholism and substance abuse: Strategies for clinical intervention.* New York: The Free Press.

Hatterer, J.L. (1980) *The pleasure addicts: The addictive process—food, sex, drugs, alcohol, work and more.* New York: A.S. Barnes and Company.

Hoffman, S., & Hoffman, I. (1970) "The will to grandeur: de Gaulle as political artist". in D.A. Rustow (ed.), *Philosophers and kings: Studies in leadership.* New York: Braziller.

Holden, C., (1985) "Genes, personality and alcoholism: Some people may inherit a vulnerability to a severe form of alcoholism". In

W.B. Rucker & M.E. Rucker (Eds.) *Drugs, Society and Behavior 89/90*. Guildford: The Dushkin Publishing Group.

Hollidge, C. (1980). Psychodynamic aspects of the addicted personality and their treatment in the therapeutic community. In Readings "Congresbroek 5e Werelflonferentie van therapeutiwsche gemeenchappen", Samsom Sijthoff, Alphen aan de Rijn. In G. DeLeon & J.T. Ziegenfuss, (1986) *Therapeutic communities for addictions: Readings in theory, research and practice.* Springfield, Ill., Charles C. Thomas Pub.

House, R.J. (1977) "A 1976 theory of charismatic leadership". In J.G. Hunt & L.L. Larson (eds.), *Leadership: The cutting edge.* Cargondale: Southern Illinois University Press.

Howell, J.M. (1985) *A laboratory study of charismatic leadership.* Paper presented at annual meeting of the Academy of Management, San Diego, Calif., August.

Hundleby, J.D. (1979) *Individual and environmental predictors and correlates of adolescent drug-related behavior. Report on Project 1212—5–126,* Non-Medical Use of Drugs Directorate, Ottawa, Canada. In T.E. Bratter & G.G. Forest, (1985) *Alcoholism and substance abuse: Strategies for clinical intervention.* New York: The Free Press.

Jaffe, J.H. "Drug addiction and drug abuse". (1975) In L.S. Goodman & A. Gilman (Eds.), *The pharmacological basis of therapeutics, 5th ed.* New York: Macmillan Publishing Co.

Jurick, N.C. (1987). "Persuasion in Self-help Groups". *Small Group Behavior.* Vol. 18 No. 3, 368–397.

Keichel, W., III. (1983) "Wanted: Corporate leaders". *Fortune,* May 30, pp. 135–140.

Khantzian, E.J., Mack, J.E., & Schatzber, A.F. (1974) "Heroin use as an attempt to cope: Clinical observations". *American Journal of Psychiatry,* 131, 160–164. In T.E. Bratter & G.G. Forest, (1985) *Alcoholism and substance abuse: Strategies for clinical intervention.* New York: The Free Press.

Lowen, A. (1985) *Narcissism: Denial of the true self.* New York: Collier Books.

McClelland, D.C. (1975) *Power: The inner experience.* New York: Irvington.

McMahon, E.M., & Campbell, P.A. (1967) *Becoming a person in the whole Christ.* New York: Sheed and Ward.

Mehr, J. (1980) *Human services: Concepts and intervention strategies.* Boston: Allyn & Bacon.

Midanik, L. (1983) "Familial alcoholism and problem drinking in a national drinking practices survey". *Addictive Behaviors* 8, 133–141. In T.E. Bratter & G.G. Forest, (1985) *Alcoholism and sub-*

stance abuse: Strategies for clinical intervention. New York: The Free Press.

Milkman, H., & Frosch, W. (1980) "Theory of drug use". In D.J. Lettieri, M. Sayers, & H.W. Pearson (eds.), *Theories on drug abuse: Selected contemporary perspectives.* National Institute on Drug Abuse Research Monograph no. 30. Rockville, Md: National Institute on Alcohol Abuse and Alcoholism.

Nietzsche, F. (1974) "Thus spoke Zarathustra". In O. Levy (ed.), *The complete works of Friedrich Nietzche.* New York: Gordon Press, (Originally published 1883.)

Nikken, C. (1988) *The addictive personality: Understanding compulsion in our lives.* San Francisco: Harper & Row.

Nineteen Eighty-nine, 1967–1989, 25th Anniversary, 1989 (Yearbook)

Nouwen, H.J. (1971) *Creative Ministry.* New York: Image Books.

Pattison, E.M., Sobell, M.B., Sobell, L.C. (1977) *Emerging concepts of alcohol dependence.* New York: Springer Publishing Company.

Peck, M.S. (1987) *The different drum: Community making and peace.* New York: Simon & Schuster Inc.

Peele, S. (1975) *Love and addiction.* New York: New American Library Inc.

Peele, S. (1985) *The meaning of addiction: Compulsive experience and its interpretation.* Lexington: Lexington Books. Peele, S. (1989) *Out of the habit trap.* In W.B. Rucker & M.E. Rucker (Eds.) *Drugs, Society and Behavior 89/90.* Guildford: The Dushkin Publishing Group.

Romeder, J.M. (1982) *Self-Help Groups in Canada.* Ottawa: Health and WelfareCanada.

Ryan, P. (1990) Written communication to author, Windsor, Ont.

Schaef, A.W. (1987) *When society becomes an addict.* San Francisco: Harper & Row Publishers.

Schaef, A.W. (1989) *Escape from intimacy: The pseudo-relationship addictions.* Untangling the "Love Addictions": Sex, romance, relationships. New York: Harper & Row.

Schuckit, M.A. (1971) Depression and alcoholism in women. Proceedings, First Annual Alcoholism Conference of the NIAAA. Washington, D.C.: U.S. Government Printing Office. In T.E. Bratter & G.G. Forest, (1985) *Alcoholism and substance abuse: Strategies for clinical intervention.* New York: The Free Press.

Selby, S. (1989) Personal communication to author, Windsor, Ont.

Shaffer, H. Kauffman, J. (1985) "The clinical assessment and diagnosis of addiction". In Bratter, T.E., & Forrest, G.G. (1985) *Alcoholism and substance abuse: strategies for clinical intervention.* New York: The Free Press.

Skinner, H.A., Jackson, D.N., & Hoffman, H. "Alcoholic personality types: Identification and correlates". *Journal of Abnormal Psychology*, 1974, 83, 645–866 (1974).

Skinner, H.A., Reed, P.A., & Jackson, D.N. (1976) "Toward the objective diagnosis of psychopathology: Generalizability of modal personality profiles". *Journal of Consulting and Clinical Psychology*, 1976, 44, 111–117.

Smith, B.J. (1982) *An initial test of a theory of charismatic leadership based on the response of subordinates.* Unpublished doctoral dissertation, Faculty of Management, University of Toronto.

Swinson, J.S. (1980) "Sex differences in the inheritance of alcoholism". In O.J. Kalant (Ed.) "Alcohol and drug problems in women". *American Journal of Psychiatry*.

The Brentwood News (1989) Volume 2, No. 1, Feb. 1989. The New American Bible (1970). New York, N.Y.: P.J. Kenedy & Sons.

Trice, H.M. & Beyer, J.M. (1986) "Charisma and its routinization in two social movement organizations". *Research in Organizational Behavior*, 8, 113–164.

Tucker, R.C. (1970) "The theory of charismatic leadership". In D.A. Rustow (ed.), *Philosophers and Kings: Studies in Leadership.* New York: Braziller.

Vaillant, G.E., & Milofskey, E.S. (1982) "The etiology of alcoholism: A prospective viewpoint". *American Psychologist* 37: 494–503. In S. Peele (1985) *The meaning of addiction: Compulsive experience and its interpretation.* Lexington: Lexington Books.

Vaillant, G.E. (1983) *The natural history of alcoholism.* Cambridge, MA: Harvard University Press. Peele, S. (1985) *The meaning of addiction: Compulsive experience and its interpretation.* Lexington: Lexington Books.

Vanier, J. (1985) *Man and woman He made them.* Mahwah, N.Y.: Paulist Press.

Weber, M. (1947) *The theory of social and economic organization.* (A.M. Henderson & T. Parson, trans.; T. Parsons, (ed.) New York: Free Press. (Originally published 1924.)

Wegsdcheider, S. (1981) *Another Chance: Hope and health for the alcoholic family.* Palo Alto: Science and Behavior Books Inc.

Willner, A.R. (1968) *Charismatic political leadership: A theory.* Princeton, N.J.: Center for International Studies, Princeton University.

Glossary of Terms Used at Brentwood

Alcoholic	A person with a "people problem" whose life predicament renders him\her blind to the presence of other people and unable to give or receive respect, caring or love.
Alcoholism	In the Brentwood tradition, a spiritual form of blindness which prevents a person from being whole. It creates barriers which induce fear, timidity, worry, panic, illusion, hostility, desolation, despair and in its most regressive stage, self-destruction and suicide.
Ask, Listen and Do What You're Told	Alcoholics have been so incapacitated in their mistaken notion of right and wrong and their distortion of reality that they require the careful guidance and instruction of Fr. Paul or the counselling staff until they develop a clear insight into the truth of themselves and others and until they learn to choose and carry out sound decisions.
Closed Heart	A figurative expression which symbolizes the prison walls which the alcoholic erects as a form of protection from the painfulness of living a fully human existence. It is embodied in excessive loneliness, isolation and self-deprivation.
Consulting	The process of seeking skilled direction and competent advice on major issues from Fr. Paul or the counselling staff for the purpose of bringing peace and balance into one's life.
Fellowship	The Brentwood followers who are constructively engaged as a family in the process of spiritual growth and development.

199

Fraternizing	Engaging in conversation or written or verbal communication with certain specified members of the opposite sex, especially those on program while involved with the Brentwood program.
Free Will	Is the capacity to choose after wise consultation and deliberation. It furnishes a person with the ability to make responsible decisions in terms of one's life and in reference to one's relationship to others.
Graduate	A person who has completed the ninety-day program and is committed to the Brentwood way of life.
God's Will	Is contained in the "Our Father" which is a pathway to the "Kingdom of God" here on earth "as it is in heaven." It is the process of submitting to a power greater than oneself and is a means to love, freedom and fulfillment.
Inventories	A series of written submissions which commence in the fifth week of program where residents provide a written account of issues from the past or present which are critically troublesome to them.
Me, Me, Me	An inordinate egocentric preoccupation with the self which dismisses the need for other people in one's life and which blinds a person to his or her own growth.
One-day-at-a-time	Living effectively in the present without being needlessly obsessed with past anxiety or future worries.
Our Father	Brentwood is seen as a family which has a strong allegiance to a loving Father who compassionately affirms our being. The "Our Father" is recited daily in unison following the various group meetings as a form of praise and gratitude for one's spiritual growth and development. The "Our Father" is seen as a blueprint and guideline for defining how a caring community life of brothers and sisters should be lived in an untiring bond of "other-centered-love."
One-on-ones	An encounter consisting of two people which provides for honesty and mutual self-disclosure.

Part Of	A sense of belonging to a process which is greater than oneself and which affords an opportunity for the enhancement of self-worth and self-esteem.
People Needing People	A motto and way of life which characterizes the Brentwood spirit of caring, sharing and confiding which is analogous and consistent with the laws of God and of nature.
Poor Me's	An unhealthy negative attitude and unremittent sense of self-pity which limits a person's engagement with other people and prevents him or her from being "part of." In the alcoholic this is usually camouflaged with resentments, hostility and hatred.
Reacting	An excessively negative and destructive way of conveying to others one's intense displeasure and indignation which not only erects a barrier and obstacle to trust and dialogue but which subsequently promotes turmoil, confusion and discouragement.
Responding	A healthy and constructive way of relating to people, places and things with notable discretion, enthusiasm and cooperation.
Relapse	The process of regressing to one's former way of thinking, feeling and behaviour which sometimes entails the consumption of drugs and alcohol.
Self-will	The deliberate act of defying God and other people and of feeding into the disease of alcoholism by restricting one's inherent capacity to think, feel and behave in a "growth directed" manner.
Sharing	The process of mutual disclosure which is integrally related to one's feelings and emotions as opposed to being predominantly "heady" and cerebral. It provides an opportunity for the head and the heart to be in harmony and balance.
Sobriety	A complete and total commitment to abstinence from drugs and alcohol for those who have gone through program and have graduated from Brentwood.

Special	Applying to oneself inordinate qualities of pretentiousness and grandiosity which prevent one from authentic encounters of growth and fellowship in the normal and ordinary affairs of life.
Spiritual	At Brentwood this is an indispensable belief which maintains that people need one another for their growth and fulfillment. The spiritual communicates a "language of the heart" and is personified by mutual understanding, shared compassion, caring confrontation and reciprocal growth. The strength, unity, balance and wisdom which is derived from fellowship are all spiritual ingredients which are generously experienced at Brentwood on a daily basis.
Transformation	A dramatic change from one's former destructive lifestyle of thinking, feeling and behaving to a newly energized manner of fulfilling one's potential and of "being there" for others. It means relinquishing certain companions, places and circumstances so as to enhance one's spiritual recovery.